It's another great book from CGP...

GCSE Additional Applied Science is all about **understanding how science works**. And not only that — understanding it well enough to be able to **question** what you hear on TV and read in the papers.

But don't panic. This book includes all the **science facts** you need to learn, and shows you how they work in the real world. It even includes a **free** Online Edition you can read on your computer or tablet.

How to get your free Online Edition

Just go to **cgpbooks.co.uk/extras** and enter this code...

0444 4740 2551 3297

By the way, this code only works for one person. If somebody else has used this book before you, they might have already claimed the Online Edition.

CGP — still the best! ☺

Our sole aim here at CGP is to produce the highest quality books — carefully written, immaculately presented and dangerously close to being funny.

Then we work our socks off to get them out to you — at the cheapest possible prices.

Contents

Published by CGP

From original material by Richard Parsons.

Editors:
Katie Braid, Mary Falkner, Helen Ronan, Camilla Simson, Hayley Thompson, Megan Tyler.

Contributors:
Giles Greenway, Andy Rankin, Claire Reed, Sophie Watkins.

ISBN: 978 1 84762 884 8

With thanks to Barrie Crowther, Helena Hayes, Rosie McCurrie and Philip Rushworth
for the proofreading.
With thanks to Anna Lupton for the copyright research.

www.cgpbooks.co.uk

Printed by Elanders Ltd, Newcastle upon Tyne.

Clipart from Corel®

The Scientific Process

For your <u>exams</u> and your <u>assignments</u>, you need to know about how the world of science works.

Science is All About <u>Testing Hypotheses</u>

Scientists make an observation.

1) Scientists <u>OBSERVE</u> (look at) something they don't understand, e.g. an illness.
2) They carry out <u>RESEARCH</u> and come up with a <u>possible explanation</u> for what they've observed.
3) This explanation is called a <u>HYPOTHESIS</u>.

Hundreds of years ago, we thought demons caused illness.

They test their hypothesis.

4) Next, they test whether the hypothesis is <u>right or wrong</u>.
5) They do this by making a <u>PREDICTION</u> — a statement based on the hypothesis that can be tested.
6) They then <u>TEST</u> this prediction by carrying out <u>experiments</u> or <u>tests</u>.

They analyse the evidence.

7) Scientists need to analyse all the <u>data</u> they've collected from their experiments and make <u>conclusions</u>.
8) If the data shows that their prediction was right, this is <u>EVIDENCE</u> that their <u>hypothesis might be right</u> too.

Then we thought it was caused by 'bad blood' and treated it with leeches).

They let other scientists know.

9) Once a scientist has a conclusion and a <u>procedure</u> (method) to follow, they tell the <u>scientific community</u> (other scientists) all about it.
10) Then, other scientists carry out <u>more experiments</u> to test the hypothesis.
11) Sometimes these scientists will find <u>more evidence</u> that the <u>hypothesis is RIGHT</u>.
12) Sometimes they'll find <u>evidence</u> that shows the <u>hypothesis is WRONG</u>.

The explanation is accepted or rejected.

13) If <u>all the evidence</u> that's been found <u>supports</u> the <u>hypothesis</u>, it becomes an <u>ACCEPTED THEORY</u> and goes into <u>textbooks</u> for people to learn.
14) If the <u>evidence</u> shows that the hypothesis is <u>wrong</u>, scientists must:
   - <u>Change the hypothesis</u>, OR
   - Come up with a <u>new hypothesis</u>.

Now we know most illnesses are due to microorganisms.

<u>You expect me to believe that — then show me the evidence...</u>

<u>If scientists think something is true, they need to produce evidence to convince others — it's all part of <u>testing a hypothesis</u>. Along the way some hypotheses will be <u>disproved</u> (shown not to be true).

Following Standard Procedures

This section is all about how scientists work safely when they carry out <u>practical tasks</u>. But first things first, they have to be able to follow a <u>procedure</u>. Whether making acids or measuring giraffes, scientists follow '<u>standard procedures</u>' — clear instructions describing exactly how to carry out these practical tasks.

Standard Procedures Mean Everyone Does Things the Same Way

1) Once a scientist has come up with a <u>hypothesis</u> (see page 1) they carry out <u>experiments</u> to test it.

2) They must carry out their experiments using <u>standard procedures</u>.

3) Standard procedures are <u>agreed methods of working</u> — they are chosen because they're the <u>safest</u>, <u>most effective</u> and <u>accurate methods</u> to use.

4) Using standard procedures means that everyone who carries out an experiment does it the <u>same way</u> — this helps to make the results <u>consistent</u>.

5) Standard procedures can be agreed <u>within a company</u>, <u>nationally</u>, or <u>internationally</u>.

There are Six Steps to Following a Standard Procedure

When following a standard procedure, you need to:

1) <u>Read the procedure</u> and check you <u>understand</u> everything.

2) Complete a <u>risk assessment</u> for the activity (see page 4).

> There aren't that many risks associated with this experiment (there are no <u>dangerous chemicals</u> or <u>risks of explosions</u>). The biggest risk is the possibility of dropping <u>heavy weights</u> onto your feet.

> **Densicorp Standard Procedure for Measuring the Density of Materials:**
>
> 1) Ensure test specimens have a regular shape (e.g. cubes or cylinders).
> 2) Measure the specimen's mass to the nearest 0.01 g.
> 3) Measure the specimen's dimensions to the nearest mm.
> 4) Calculate the volume of the specimen.
> 5) Calculate the density of the specimen using the formula:
>   density = mass ÷ volume.

3) <u>Collect the equipment and materials</u> you need, and set out your working area.

> You'll need a <u>top pan balance</u>, a <u>ruler</u> and some <u>materials</u> to measure.

4) Select instruments that have an <u>appropriate sensitivity</u>, and use them to make <u>accurate observations</u> or <u>measurements</u>.

> Your balance will need to be able to <u>accurately</u> measure to the <u>nearest 0.01 g</u>, and your ruler to the <u>nearest mm</u>.

5) Follow the instructions <u>one step at a time</u>.

6) Identify possible sources of <u>error</u> and <u>repeat observations</u> and <u>measurements</u> where necessary to improve <u>reliability</u>.

> Before packing away all your equipment have a look over your <u>results</u> — if you have any <u>anomalous results</u>, repeat the experiment and have a <u>think</u> about why they might have been <u>wrong</u>.

An anomalous result is one that doesn't seem to fit with all the rest. See page 86.

After the Experiment Scientists Draw Conclusions

1) Scientists use the <u>evidence</u> they collect in their experiments to draw <u>conclusions</u>.

2) They then have to <u>present</u> their evidence and their conclusions in a <u>report</u> so that other scientists can read about it.

Tamoto techkup — a sauce of error...

There are so many reasons why you should follow <u>standard procedures</u>. They're <u>tried and tested</u>, so you're more likely to get <u>accurate</u> and <u>reliable results</u> and less likely to <u>injure yourself</u>. They should have them for everything, like getting dressed — there are more 'trouser-related accidents' every year than you'd think.

Avoiding Hazards

Scientific work can be <u>dangerous</u>. You need to be able to work <u>safely</u> in order to <u>prevent</u> accidents from happening. This applies to all workplaces, e.g. school and industrial labs.

Hazard Symbols *Show if Something is* <u>Dangerous</u>

Hazards need to be <u>identified</u> so that they can be <u>avoided</u>. <u>Hazard symbols</u> are used to show <u>if</u> something is dangerous and <u>why</u>. Here are some of the main hazard symbols you need to know:

 <u>Flammable</u> — <u>Catch fire</u> easily, e.g. petrol.

 <u>Irritant</u> — Can cause <u>reddening or blistering</u> of the skin, e.g. sodium hydroxide.

 <u>Toxic</u> — Can cause <u>death</u> either by being <u>swallowed</u>, <u>breathed</u> in, or <u>absorbed</u> through the skin, e.g. cyanide.

 <u>Harmful</u> — Like toxic but <u>not quite as dangerous</u>, e.g. copper sulfate.

 <u>Explosive</u> — can <u>explode</u> — BANG, e.g. some peroxides.

 <u>Radioactive</u> — Gives off <u>radiation</u>, e.g. plutonium.

 <u>Oxidising</u> — These provide <u>oxygen</u>, which allows other materials to <u>burn more fiercely</u>, e.g. liquid oxygen.

 <u>Biohazard</u> — Contains <u>biological</u> material that could be <u>harmful</u>, e.g. bacteria.

 <u>Dangerous for the environment</u> — Can damage the environment, e.g. ammonia.

 <u>Electrical Hazard</u> — Could give you an electric shock, e.g. power supplies.

Safety Signs *Help Keep You* Safe *in the* <u>Workplace</u>

<u>Safety signs</u> are used to give <u>health</u> and <u>safety</u> information in the <u>workplace</u>. There are <u>two</u> types:

1) <u>Mandatory signs</u> give you <u>instructions</u> that you <u>must</u> follow to stay <u>safe</u>. For example:

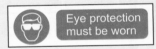 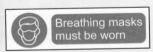
 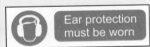

2) <u>Safe condition signs</u> mark the location of things you might need in an <u>emergency</u>. For example:

Know *Which Type* of *Fire Extinguisher* to Use

You can put out <u>small</u> fires using a <u>fire extinguisher</u>. There are <u>four main types</u> of hand-held fire extinguisher. All new fire extinguishers are painted red with a <u>colour-coded</u> band or panel to identify its <u>contents</u> and the <u>type of fire</u> it can be used on. It's important to use the <u>right fire extinguisher</u> for the type of fire — you could make the <u>fire worse</u> if you use the <u>wrong one</u>.

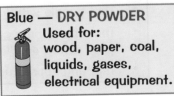 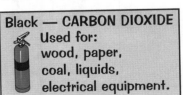 

Red — WATER Used for: wood, paper, coal.

Black — CARBON DIOXIDE Used for: wood, paper, coal, liquids, electrical equipment.

Cream — FOAM Used for: wood, paper, coal, liquids.

Blue — DRY POWDER Used for: wood, paper, coal, liquids, gases, electrical equipment.

Risk — *not just a thrilling board game...*

t's really important to pay attention to <u>hazard symbols</u> and <u>safety signs</u> — if you don't, you're just asking for <u>trouble</u>. So don't just learn these signs for the exam and then forget them. They could save your life.

Health and Safety

There are lots of <u>regulations</u> in place to protect people who work in potentially <u>hazardous</u> environments (like science labs). It's up to both the <u>employees</u> and the <u>employers</u> (or <u>students</u> and <u>teachers</u>) to make sure that everyone <u>follows</u> the regulations and that all work is done <u>safely</u>.

There are <u>Laws</u> to Make Sure People are <u>Safe</u> at Work

1) The <u>Health and Safety at Work Act (1974)</u> is a piece of <u>legislation</u> (a set of laws) that deals with <u>occupational</u> health and safety (health and safety at work).

2) The <u>Health and Safety Executive</u> (HSE) is an organisation set up by the UK government to protect people's health at their school or workplace.

3) The HSE <u>checks</u> that the <u>rules</u> given in the Health and Safety at Work Act (1974) are being followed.

Hmm... Where did my bacteria sample go?

When You <u>Plan</u> an Experiment You Need to do a <u>Risk Assessment</u>

A <u>risk assessment</u> is an examination of what <u>could</u> cause harm in the workplace. <u>Scientists</u> have to do a risk assessment whenever they plan an experiment.

There are <u>five</u> stages to a risk assessment:

1) <u>Look</u> for hazards.
2) <u>Assess</u> who may be harmed and <u>how</u>.
3) <u>Decide what action</u>, if any, needs to be taken to <u>reduce</u> the risk.
4) <u>Document</u> the findings.
5) <u>Review</u> the risk assessment <u>regularly</u>.

If a scientist <u>hasn't</u> planned an experiment themselves, it's important that they <u>read</u> the risk assessment for that experiment <u>carefully</u> before they start.

If <u>all</u> of the measures outlined in the risk assessment are followed, it should be <u>safe</u> to do the experiment.

Example — Risk assessment for growing bacteria.

Risk	How to Reduce Risk
Glass breaking causes cuts.	Take care handling glass. Report any breakages immediately.
Contamination of people or environment with bacteria.	Avoid hand to mouth/eye contact. Wear protective clothing. Wash hands after experiment. Use aseptic procedures. Don't open culture dishes once sealed. Dispose of cultures using an autoclave.
Burns from the Bunsen burner.	Take care when using a Bunsen burner.

A <u>hazard</u> is anything that could cause harm.
The <u>risk</u> is the probability that a hazard will cause harm

Check <u>Health and Safety</u> as You're <u>Doing</u> the Experiment Too

1) Just doing a risk assessment <u>isn't</u> enough to ensure that you're working <u>safely</u> — you should check that your working area is safe <u>as you're working</u> too.

2) In your <u>school science lab</u>, this could include checking:

- That any <u>bags</u> are safely out of the way.
- That people with <u>long hair</u> have it <u>tied back</u>.
- That appropriate <u>safety equipment</u> is being used (e.g. safety goggles, heat proof mats etc.).
- That any apparatus is <u>away</u> from the <u>edge</u> of the bench.

It's better to be safe than sorry...

All this might seem pretty dull but you'll be thanking your lucky stars when some rather fetching safety glasses save you from losing your eye in a freak beaker accident. Risk assessments — know 'em, love 'em, use 'em.

Revision Summary for Section 1

Well that's Section 1 over and done with. Now that wasn't too bad was it? Only six more sections to go (and a bit about practical investigations) and you'll have finished the book. But first it's time to see if you've actually learnt anything. Have a go at these questions. If you get stuck, flick back over the last three pages — the answer will be there somewhere.

1) What are standard procedures? Why should they be used?

2) List the six steps to following a standard procedure.

3) Why is it important for scientists to write down their evidence and conclusions in a report once they have finished an experiment?

4) What do hazard symbols show?

5) What do the following hazards symbols mean?

   a)   b)   c)   d)

7) What's the difference between a mandatory sign and a safe condition sign?

8) What must you wear if you see these signs?   a)   b)   c)

9) Are the signs in Question 8 mandatory signs or safe conditions signs?

10) Which of these signs shows the location of an emergency shower?

   a)   b)   c)   d)

11) Are the signs in Question 10 mandatory signs or safe conditions signs?

12) Why is it important to choose the right type of fire extinguisher for the type of fire?

13) What do fire extinguishers with a blue band contain?

14) What do fire extinguishers with a red band contain?

15) There is an electrical fire at work. Which fire extinguisher, A, B or C, should you use to put out the fire?

16) What name is given to the set of laws that deal with health and safety at work?

17) What does HSE stand for? What does the HSE do?

18) What is a risk assessment?

19) What are the five stages to a risk assessment?

20) Give three things you should check when doing a health and safety check of your working area in a science lab.

Healthcare Scientists

Besides <u>doctors</u> and <u>nurses</u>, there's a whole army of <u>skilled people</u> out there involved in keeping us <u>fit</u> and <u>healthy</u>. This page is all about those <u>people</u> and the <u>important jobs</u> that they do.

There are Lots of *Careers in Healthcare*

<u>Healthcare scientists</u> work with <u>doctors</u> and <u>nurses</u> and play a very important role in the <u>prevention</u>, <u>diagnosis</u> and <u>treatment</u> of a wide variety of <u>medical conditions</u>. For anyone who decides they fancy a job as a <u>healthcare scientist</u> there are loads of different <u>careers</u> to choose from. For example:

PHARMACIST

1) <u>Pharmacists</u> know loads of stuff about <u>drugs</u> and <u>how they are used</u>.
2) They help patients get as much <u>benefit</u> as they can from the <u>medications</u> they are taking.
3) They can also <u>advise</u> doctors and nurses on <u>which</u> drugs would be best to treat a particular problem <u>most effectively</u>.

DIETICIAN

B. BOISSONNET/SCIENCE PHOTO LIBRARY

1) <u>Dieticians</u> use their knowledge of <u>food</u> and <u>nutrition</u> to help prevent or treat <u>medical conditions</u> that are associated with <u>food</u> and <u>eating</u>.
2) They work with people who have <u>special dietary requirements</u>, helping them to <u>identify</u> the foods that they can and can't eat.
3) They also help people who have <u>eating disorders</u>.

NUTRITIONIST

1) <u>Nutritionists</u> give people <u>information</u> on <u>food</u> and <u>nutrition</u>.
2) They help people understand what they need to <u>eat</u> to have a <u>balanced diet</u> and generally <u>stay healthy</u>.
3) <u>Sports nutritionists</u> work with <u>athletes</u> and suggest diets that could help them <u>do better</u> at their <u>sport</u>.

PHYSIOTHERAPIST

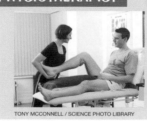

TONY MCCONNELL / SCIENCE PHOTO LIBRARY

1) <u>Physiotherapists</u> are experts on <u>joints</u> and <u>muscles</u>.
2) They help <u>treat</u> medical conditions that <u>prevent</u> people from <u>moving</u> easily, many of which are associated with <u>old age</u> (e.g. arthritis).
3) They also have an important role in <u>treating</u> and <u>rehabilitating</u> people who have had <u>serious injuries</u> (e.g. learning how to walk again after an accident).

Fitness Practitioners *Help People Keep Fit*

A fitness practitioner is someone who <u>helps people keep fit</u>. There are lots of different types. For example,

1) <u>Fitness trainers</u> supervise exercise programmes in <u>gyms</u> and <u>leisure clubs</u> and provide <u>personal training</u>.
2) <u>Coaches</u> provide <u>technical training</u> for particular sports or events, as well as <u>general fitness training</u>.
3) <u>Sports physiologists</u> help athletes improve their <u>physical fitness</u> and <u>strength</u>.

My idea of a fitness programme — running to the pie shop...

Pharmacists, dieticians, nutritionists and physiotherapists are just a few types of healthcare scientist. There are plenty of others as well, e.g. <u>radiographers</u>, <u>biomedical scientists</u> and <u>lab technicians</u> to name just a few.

The Blood and Blood Vessels

Healthcare scientists need to have a good understanding of how the body works. Different healthcare scientists need to know about different parts of the body — this page is about the blood system.

Blood is a Fluid Made up of Cells, Platelets and Plasma

Your blood is mostly made up of four different things:

1) Red blood cells — they transport oxygen from the lungs to all the cells in the body.
2) White blood cells — they help to fight infection.
3) Platelets — these help the blood to clot at the site of a wound.
4) Plasma — this is the liquid that carries everything about. E.g. glucose is carried in the plasma.

Blood is Carried Around the Body in Blood Vessels

There are three different types of blood vessel:

1) **ARTERIES** — carry the blood away from the heart.
2) **CAPILLARIES** — involved in the exchange of materials at the tissues.
3) **VEINS** — carry the blood to the heart.

Blood Vessels are Designed for Their Function

ARTERIES CARRY BLOOD UNDER PRESSURE

1) The heart pumps the blood out at high pressure, so the artery walls are strong and elastic.
2) The walls are thick compared to the size of the lumen (the hole down the middle). They contain thick layers of muscle to make them strong.
3) The high pressure means that if you press down lightly on an artery, you can feel a pulse each time the heart beats (see page 12).

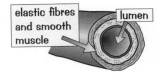

elastic fibres and smooth muscle | lumen

CAPILLARIES ARE REALLY SMALL

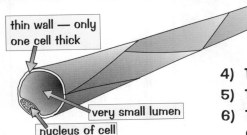

thin wall — only one cell thick

very small lumen

nucleus of cell

1) Arteries eventually branch into capillaries.
2) Capillaries are really tiny — too small to see.
3) They carry the blood really close to every cell in the body to exchange substances with them.
4) They have permeable walls, so substances can move in and out.
5) They supply nutrients and oxygen and take away waste like CO_2.
6) Their walls are only one cell thick. This increases the rate of exchange by decreasing the distance over which it happens.

VEINS TAKE BLOOD BACK TO THE HEART

1) Capillaries eventually join up to form veins.
2) The blood is at lower pressure in the veins so the walls don't need to be as thick as artery walls.
3) They have a bigger lumen than arteries to help the blood flow despite the lower pressure.
4) They also have valves to help keep the blood flowing in the right direction.

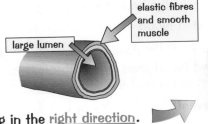

elastic fibres and smooth muscle

large lumen

Learn this page — don't struggle in vein...

This is more like it, a bit of proper biology to sink your teeth into — it only gets better from here on in.

The Heart

The <u>heart</u> is a <u>pump</u> that moves blood around the body. Healthcare scientists such as <u>cardiac physiologists</u> need to know how the <u>heart</u> works so that they can <u>monitor</u>, <u>diagnose</u> and <u>help</u> people with heart problems.

The Heart Pumps Blood Around the Body

1) The heart is made up of <u>two</u> separate <u>pumps</u>.
2) The <u>right side</u> of the heart <u>pumps blood</u> to the <u>lungs</u>.
3) The <u>left side</u> of the heart <u>pumps blood</u> to the <u>rest of the body</u>.
4) The <u>heart</u>, <u>blood</u> and <u>blood vessels</u> together are called the <u>cardiovascular system</u>.

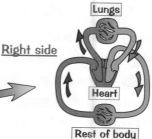

Learn This Diagram of the Heart

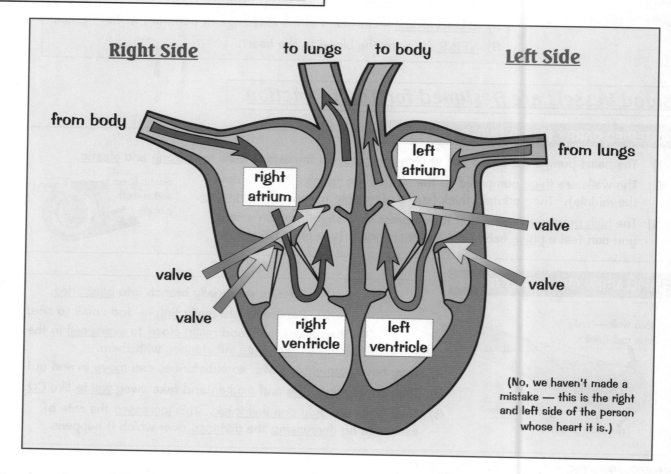

Right Side   to lungs   to body   **Left Side**

from body

right atrium

left atrium

from lungs

valve

valve

valve

valve

right ventricle

left ventricle

(No, we haven't made a mistake — this is the right and left side of the person whose heart it is.)

1) The <u>right atrium</u> of the heart receives <u>deoxygenated</u> blood (blood without any oxygen) from the <u>body</u>.
2) The deoxygenated blood moves through to the <u>right ventricle</u>, which pumps it to the <u>lungs</u>.
3) The <u>left atrium</u> receives <u>oxygenated</u> blood (oxygen rich blood) from the <u>lungs</u>.
4) The oxygenated blood then moves through to the <u>left ventricle</u>, which pumps it out round the <u>whole body</u>.
5) The <u>valves</u> prevent the <u>backflow</u> of blood.

Heart

You won't get any marks in the exam if you label a heart like this. Sorry.

Okay — let's get to the heart of the matter...

The human heart <u>beats</u> 100 000 times a day on average. You can measure it by taking your <u>pulse</u> (see page 12).

The Lungs and Breathing

You need to get air (containing <u>oxygen</u>) into your lungs so the oxygen can get into the blood...
which is where <u>breathing</u> comes in.

The <u>Thorax</u> — <u>The</u> <u>Top</u> <u>Part of Your Body</u>

The <u>thorax</u> is the part of the 'body' from the neck down to
the diaphragm. There are a few parts you need to know...

1) The <u>lungs</u> are like big pink <u>sponges</u>.

2) The <u>trachea</u> (the pipe connecting your mouth and
   nose to your lungs) splits into two tubes called
   '<u>bronchi</u>' — one goes to each lung.

3) The bronchi split into progressively smaller tubes
   called <u>bronchioles</u> that end with small bags called
   <u>alveoli</u> — this is where oxygen moves into the
   blood and carbon dioxide moves out.

4) The <u>ribs</u> protect the lungs and the heart etc.
   They're also important in breathing (see below).

5) The <u>intercostal muscles</u> are the muscles in
   between the ribs.

6) The <u>diaphragm</u> is the large muscle at the bottom
   of the thorax, which is also important for breathing.

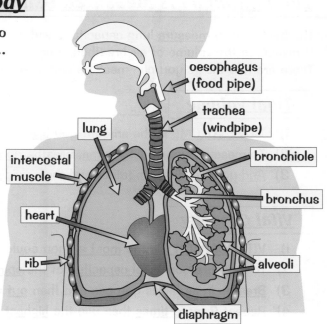

The <u>Intercostal</u> <u>Muscles and</u> <u>Diaphragm</u> <u>Make Us</u> <u>Breathe</u>

Both the <u>diaphragm</u> and <u>intercostal muscles</u> play an important role in breathing in and out.
During ventilation there is a change in <u>pressure</u> — this is what causes air to enter and leave the lungs.

Breathing IN:

1) The intercostal muscles
   <u>contract</u>, pulling the
   ribcage <u>up</u> and <u>out</u>.

2) The diaphragm <u>contracts</u>
   and flattens out.

3) The contracting muscles
   make the chest cavity
   <u>larger</u>.

4) This <u>decreases</u> the
   <u>pressure</u> inside the lungs,
   so air is drawn <u>in</u>.

Breathing OUT:

1) The intercostal muscles
   <u>relax</u> — the ribcage
   drops in and down.

2) The diaphragm <u>relaxes</u>
   and arches up.

3) The relaxing
   muscles make the
   chest cavity <u>smaller</u>.

4) This causes an increase in
   pressure inside the lungs,
   and air is forced <u>out</u>.

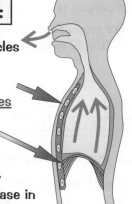

~~T~~ke a breather — there's a lung way to go yet...

~~If~~ you've ever fancied a career as a <u>sports physiologist</u> then you'll need to know this stuff inside out. Plus it comes
~~r~~eally handy in everyday life — I regularly drop interesting biology facts into conversation in an attempt to woo
~~the~~ opposite sex. Even if it doesn't go down too well, at least it's stuck in your head that air is drawn <u>into the lungs</u>
~~bec~~ause of a <u>decrease in pressure</u> caused by an <u>increased thorax volume</u>. Oh, and it'll also be useful in the exam.

Measuring Lung Capacity and Breathing Rate

Lung capacity is how much air your lungs can hold. Professionals like respiratory physiologists measure lung capacity to test for and monitor lung problems. Fitness practitioners use lung capacity to measure fitness.

Lung Capacity is Measured Using a Spirometer

The best way to measure lung capacity is with a device called a spirometer.
It measures the volume of air breathed in and out. It can also help detect lung problems, e.g. asthma.
There are two things you can measure with a spirometer that you need to know about:

Tidal Volume

1) TIDAL VOLUME is the amount you breathe in (or out) with each breath.
2) To measure your tidal volume, breathe normally into the spirometer 3 times.
3) Add your readings together and then divide by 3 to get an average tidal volume.

There are no problems with this baby's lungs

Vital Capacity

1) VITAL CAPACITY is the most air you could possibly breathe in or out in one breath.
2) To measure your vital capacity put the spirometer mouthpiece in your mouth.
3) Breathe in as far as you can and then out as far as you can.
4) Repeat 2 more times then use the highest value.

Breathing Rate is the Number of Breaths Per Minute

1) The number of breaths you take every minute is known as your breathing rate.
2) You can measure someone's breathing rate by counting the number of breaths they take in one minute.
3) But this isn't very reliable because you won't take exactly the same number of breaths every minute.
4) Instead, it's more reliable to take an average — you count the total number of breaths a person takes and then divide by the number of minutes you counted for.
5) For example, if Barry took 150 breaths in 5 minutes, his breathing rate would be 150 ÷ 5 = 30 breaths per minute.

Exercise Affects Breathing Rate and Tidal Volume

When you start to exercise, your breathing changes in two ways...

1) Your breathing rate increases — you take more breaths per minute.
2) Your tidal volume increases — you take deeper breaths.

You can monitor these changes by comparing your breathing rate and tidal volume while you're exercising with your baseline breathing rate and tidal volume (these are measured while you're resting).

Now take a deep breath and learn these facts...

If you're asthmatic, you might be used to breathing into an instrument called a peak flow meter. These measure how much force you're using to breathe out. This helps doctors to adjust the amount of medication you need to carry on with your active life and to monitor whether the medication is working. Hurrah for peak flow meters.

Respiration and Exercise

Respiration might not sound very rock 'n' roll, but it's pretty fundamental to life as we know it.

Respiration is NOT 'Breathing In and Out'

Respiration is really important — it releases the energy that cells need to do just about everything.

1) Respiration is the process of breaking down glucose to release energy.
2) When you exercise, a lot of the energy released in respiration is used to make your muscles contract.
3) The heart and lungs allow glucose and oxygen to be transported to the muscles for respiration.
4) There are two types of respiration — aerobic and anaerobic.

AEROBIC RESPIRATION NEEDS PLENTY OF OXYGEN

1) Aerobic respiration is what happens when there's plenty of oxygen available.
2) "Aerobic" just means "with oxygen" and it's the most efficient way to release energy from glucose.
3) This is the type of respiration that you're using most of the time. It turns glucose from your food and oxygen from your lungs into carbon dioxide and water — releasing loads of energy in the process:

Glucose + Oxygen ➡ Carbon Dioxide + Water (+ ENERGY)

4) The formula equation for aerobic respiration is:

$$C_6H_{12}O_6 + 6O_2 \longrightarrow 6CO_2 + 6H_2O \quad (+ \text{ENERGY})$$

Higher

ANAEROBIC RESPIRATION DOESN'T USE OXYGEN AT ALL

"Anaerobic" just means "without oxygen".

1) Anaerobic respiration happens when there's not enough oxygen available.
2) In anaerobic respiration, the break down of glucose is incomplete and lactic acid is produced.

Glucose ➡ Lactic Acid (+ ENERGY)

3) Anaerobic respiration is **NOT** the best way to convert glucose into energy because it releases much less energy than aerobic respiration.

Higher

Anaerobic Respiration Gives You an Oxygen Debt

1) When you respire anaerobically lactic acid builds up in the muscles, which can be painful.
2) After resorting to anaerobic respiration, when you stop exercising you'll have an oxygen debt — your muscles are still short of oxygen because they haven't been getting enough for a while.
3) You'll need extra oxygen to convert the lactic acid that's built up in your muscles back into glucose.
4) This means you have to keep breathing hard and your heart rate has to stay high for a while after you stop exercising — to repay the debt.

Higher

eckon aerobics classes should be called anaerobics instead...

, so when you're just sitting about, you use aerobic respiration to get all your energy — but when you do nuous exercise, you can't get enough oxygen to your muscles, so you use anaerobic respiration too.

Measuring Heart Rate and Recovery

Sports physiologists often <u>monitor</u> an athlete's <u>heart</u> and <u>breathing</u> rate before, during and after exercise. This can show how <u>fit</u> an athlete is, and what sort of <u>training programme</u> they need.

Measure Heart Rate by Taking a Pulse

1) It's hard to measure heart rate directly, but you can measure <u>pulse rate</u> instead.

2) You take someone's pulse by <u>placing two fingers</u> on their <u>wrist</u> or neck and <u>counting</u> the <u>number of pulses you feel</u> in a <u>minute</u>.

3) Each pulse is <u>one</u> heartbeat.

4) Get someone to measure your pulse when you're sitting down quietly to find your <u>baseline</u> (resting) <u>heart rate</u>. Most people have a resting heart rate of around <u>70 beats/min</u>, but it depends on how fit you are — <u>fitter</u> people have a <u>slower</u> resting heart rate.

Exercising Increases Heart Rate

1) Muscles need <u>energy</u> from respiration to <u>contract</u>. When you exercise some of your muscles contract more frequently than normal so you need <u>more energy</u>. This energy comes from <u>increased respiration</u>.

2) The increase in respiration means you need to get <u>more oxygen</u> into the cells.

3) When you <u>exercise</u>, two things happen to your heart:
   - Your <u>heart rate</u> increases — it beats more times per minute.
   - The <u>volume</u> of blood pumped each <u>heartbeat</u> increases.

4) This means that <u>oxygen</u> and <u>glucose</u> can be delivered to the <u>muscles</u> more <u>quickly</u>.

5) Your breathing rate and tidal volume (see page 10) also increase to try and get <u>more oxygen into</u> the blood and <u>more CO_2 out</u> of the blood.

6) When you do <u>really vigorous exercise</u> (like sprinting) your body can't supply <u>oxygen</u> to your muscles quickly enough, so they start <u>respiring anaerobically</u> (see previous page).

Recovery Time Depends on Fitness

1) Your <u>recovery time</u> is the time it takes your body to get back to normal after exercise.

2) It depends on how <u>strenuous</u> the exercise was, and how <u>fit</u> you are.

YOU CAN MEASURE YOUR RECOVERY TIME IN AN EXPERIMENT

1) Measure your <u>pulse rate</u> at <u>rest</u>.

2) <u>Run</u> about for <u>20 minutes</u>.

3) Measure your pulse rate <u>every two minutes</u> till it's back to <u>normal</u>.

4) The <u>time</u> it takes from when you <u>stop</u> exercising for your pulse to go back to <u>normal</u> is your <u>recovery time</u>.

5) You could also do a similar experiment using <u>breathing rate</u>.

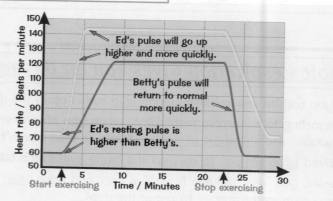

Ed's pulse will go up higher and more quickly.

Betty's pulse will return to normal more quickly.

Ed's resting pulse is higher than Betty's.

Betty's fit.

Ed's unfit.

All this talk of exercise is making me feel tired...

Many athletes these days use an <u>electronic</u> heart rate monitor that straps onto their wrist or chest. This means they can measure their heart rate <u>while</u> they're exercising, then <u>download</u> the data onto a computer and analyse it. It's quite tricky taking your pulse when you're in the middle of a marathon.

Body Temperature

Your <u>body temperature</u> needs to stay roughly the same for you to be healthy. Fortunately, there are <u>control systems</u> in the body which <u>cool</u> you down if you get too <u>hot</u> and <u>heat</u> you up if you get too <u>cold</u>.

Body Temperature **Can be Measured Using a** Thermometer

You can measure your body temperature using a thermometer. There are various types of <u>thermometer</u> that can be used to record body temperature:

1) A <u>clinical thermometer</u> — a bog standard thermometer that you stick under your armpit or tongue.

2) An <u>electronic digital thermometer</u> — a fancy thermometer that you put in your ear — it gives a digital reading.

3) A <u>liquid crystal thermometer</u> — a plastic strip that's placed on the skin (usually on the forehead) and changes colour to show the temperature.

Normal body temperature is around 37 °C. If your body temperature is higher than this you could be ill.

Body Temperature **is Controlled by the** Brain

1) There's a <u>thermoregulatory centre</u> in the <u>brain</u> which acts as your own <u>personal thermostat</u> — it <u>monitors</u> and <u>controls</u> your body temperature.

2) To keep your body at the right temperature, it does these things:

When You're TOO HOT:

1) Your body makes <u>lots of sweat</u> — when it <u>evaporates</u> it <u>transfers heat</u> to the environment, cooling you down.

2) The <u>blood vessels</u> that supply the skin capillaries <u>dilate</u> (get wider). This allows <u>more blood</u> to flow near the <u>surface</u>, so it can <u>lose more heat</u> into the surroundings.

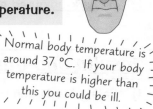

Skin capillaries are tiny blood vessels close to the surface of the skin.

When You're TOO COLD:

1) Your body makes <u>very little sweat</u>.

2) The <u>blood vessels</u> that supply the skin capillaries <u>constrict</u> (get narrow). This means that <u>less heat</u> can be <u>lost</u> from the blood to the surroundings, as <u>less blood</u> can flow near the <u>surface</u> of the skin.

dy temperature... don't sweat it

there you have it. Learn this and the next time you forget your anti-perspirant after P.E. you'll know all about
sweating helps to keep your <u>inside conditions</u> nice and <u>constant</u>. It won't stop your mates avoiding you, but
can't have everything — and at least knowing about it might pick you up some marks in the exam.

Controlling Water and Glucose

Your body has to work quite <u>hard</u> to keep the levels of all the things that pass in and out nice and <u>stable</u>. This page is about how your body regulates two <u>really important</u> substances — <u>water</u> and <u>glucose</u>.

We Need to Balance Our Water Content

The body <u>constantly</u> has to <u>balance</u> the water coming in against the water going out. Water is taken into the body as <u>food and drink</u> and is <u>lost</u> from the body in <u>three main ways</u>:

1) In <u>urine</u>   2) In <u>sweat</u>   3) In <u>faeces</u>.

The kidneys control how much water is in our bodies by changing the amount of urine we produce.

food and drink

sweat

urine   faeces

- When we're hydrated (e.g. after drinking a lot), the kidneys produce <u>more urine</u> and the urine will be <u>pale</u> and <u>dilute</u>.

- When we're dehydrated (e.g. on a hot day when we're producing lots of sweat), the kidneys produce <u>less urine</u> and the urine will be <u>dark-coloured</u> and <u>concentrated</u>.

> We're dehydrated when we don't have enough water in our bodies.

Insulin and Glucagon Control Blood Sugar Levels

1) Eating foods rich in <u>carbohydrate</u> puts a lot of <u>glucose</u> into the blood from the <u>gut</u>.

2) Normal <u>respiration</u> (see page 11) in cells <u>removes</u> glucose from the blood.

3) Vigorous <u>exercise</u> also removes a lot of glucose from the blood.

4) Levels of glucose in the blood must be kept <u>steady</u>. <u>Changes</u> in blood glucose are monitored and controlled by the <u>pancreas</u>, using hormones.

5) If circulating blood glucose levels get <u>too high</u> (e.g. just after a big meal) the pancreas releases a <u>hormone</u> called <u>insulin</u>.

6) Insulin stimulates the <u>liver</u> to <u>take up</u> glucose from the blood and <u>store</u> it as an <u>insoluble carbohydrate</u> called <u>glycogen</u>.

> If something is insoluble it means it won't dissolve.

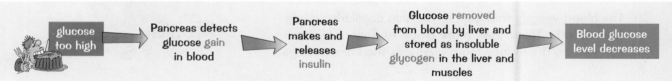

glucose too high → Pancreas detects glucose gain in blood → Pancreas makes and releases insulin → Glucose removed from blood by liver and stored as insoluble glycogen in the liver and muscles → Blood glucose level decreases

7) If circulating blood glucose levels get <u>too low</u> (e.g. following exercise) the pancreas releases <u>glucagon</u>.

8) Glucagon is a <u>hormone</u> that stimulates the <u>liver</u> to <u>break glycogen down</u> into glucose. The <u>glucose</u> is then <u>released</u> back into the bloodstream.

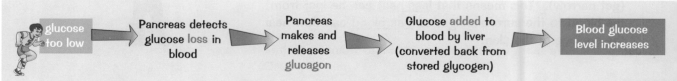

glucose too low → Pancreas detects glucose loss in blood → Pancreas makes and releases glucagon → Glucose added to blood by liver (converted back from stored glycogen) → Blood glucose level increases

Higher

My glucose levels are falling — pass the biscuits...

If you're exercising hard, make sure you <u>drink</u> enough water, to make up for what you're losing in <u>sweat</u>. Getting <u>dehydrated</u> can be really unpleasant and <u>dangerous</u>, and you won't be able to do your best in any sport if you're short of water. Don't drink too much water, though, cos that's bad too... Hmmm, tricky.

Measuring Glucose and Muscle Strength

You need to know how to carry out the following tests for the <u>exam</u>, but no one's going to ask you to wee on a stick or anything. <u>Don't</u> go testing your blood at home either — it wouldn't be a great idea.

Glucose Levels are Measured Using Dipsticks

You can test <u>urine</u> and <u>blood</u> to measure <u>glucose levels</u>. People with <u>diabetes</u> (a disease where you don't produce enough <u>insulin</u>) have to measure their blood glucose levels <u>regularly</u>.

TESTING URINE

1) Dip a <u>glucose test strip</u> (dipstick) into a urine sample.

2) Compare it against the manufacturer's <u>colour chart</u> — this shows if glucose is present.

3) There <u>shouldn't be any glucose</u> in your urine — a <u>positive result</u> might mean that you have <u>diabetes</u>.

CORDELIA MOLLOY / SCIENCE PHOTO LIBRARY

TESTING BLOOD

SATURN STILLS / SCIENCE PHOTO LIBRARY

1) <u>Prick</u> your finger using a special sterile 'pen'.

2) Put a <u>drop</u> of blood onto a <u>blood glucose test strip</u>.

3) Compare it to the manufacturer's <u>colour chart</u>.

4) The strip turns a different colour depending on how much glucose is present.

5) This helps a <u>diabetic</u> work out how much <u>insulin</u> to inject.

6) You can also get <u>digital</u> blood glucose meters that give a more <u>accurate</u> reading.

Muscle Strength is Measured Using the Grip Test

You can test the <u>strength</u> of your <u>forearm</u> and <u>hand</u> muscles using a <u>handgrip dynamometer</u>. This is sometimes used as a measure of how much <u>overall muscle strength</u> you have.

1) <u>Adjust</u> the dynamometer to match your hand size.

2) Hold the handgrip dynamometer in your <u>right hand</u> (if you're right-handed) in line with your forearm, with your elbow at a right angle to your body.

3) <u>Grip</u> the dynamometer as hard as you can. <u>Repeat</u> 3 times.

4) Record the <u>best</u> reading (usually in <u>kg</u>). <u>Average</u> strengths are about 26-31 kg for women, and 46-51 kg for men, but it varies a lot.

Sports coaches and fitness trainers can use the grip test to monitor the strength of their athletes.

You can <u>repeat</u> this test over a period of strength training, to monitor your <u>progress</u>.

The handgrip test is also used to assess <u>wrist</u> and <u>hand injuries</u>, and how they're responding to <u>treatment</u>.

you don't know these tests, urine big trouble...

me people use the <u>grip test</u> to show <u>overall muscle strength</u>. That isn't really <u>valid</u>, because it only tests your d and forearm muscles. People in <u>certain jobs</u> usually have a strong handgrip, e.g. <u>plumbers</u>, but it <u>doesn't</u> an that the rest of their muscles are as strong as Superman on steroids...

Bones, Muscles and Joints

If you do sport you're bound to get an <u>injury</u> at some point. It's really important that <u>healthcare scientists</u> like <u>physiotherapists</u> know how the body works so that they can decide on the best type of <u>treatment</u> for yo

Muscles Pull on Bones to Move Them

1) The job of a <u>skeleton</u> is to <u>support</u> the body and allow it to <u>move</u> — as well as <u>protect</u> vital <u>organs</u>.

2) A point where two or more bones meet is called a <u>joint</u>.

3) Joints allow limbs to be <u>moved</u> in different <u>directions</u>.

4) The bones at a joint are held together by <u>ligaments</u>, which stabilise the joint.

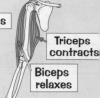

ligaments

5) Bones are attached to <u>muscles</u> by <u>tendons</u>.

6) Muscles move bones at a joint by <u>contracting</u> (becoming <u>shorter</u>).

7) Tendons <u>can't stretch</u> much so when a muscle contracts it <u>pulls</u> on the bone.

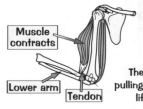

Muscle contracts

Lower arm | Tendon

The muscle contracts, pulling on the tendon, which lifts the lower arm.

Muscles Usually Come in Antagonistic Pairs

1) Muscles can only <u>pull</u> on bones to move a joint — they <u>can't</u> push.

2) This is why muscles usually come in <u>pairs</u> (called <u>antagonistic pairs</u>).

3) When one muscle in the pair contracts, the joint moves in one direction. When the other contracts, it moves in the <u>opposite</u> direction.

4) The <u>biceps</u> and <u>triceps</u> are an antagonistic pair of muscles: When the <u>biceps contracts</u>, the <u>triceps relaxes</u> and the lower arm moves <u>upwards</u>. When the <u>triceps contracts</u>, the <u>biceps relaxes</u> and the lower arm is pulled back <u>down</u>.

5) Together, they make the arm work as a <u>lever</u>, where the elbow is the pivot (see page 17).

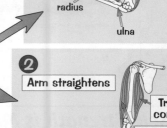

1 Arm bends

humerus

Biceps contracts

Triceps relaxes

radius

ulna

2 Arm straightens

Triceps contracts

Biceps relaxes

People can also come in antagonistic pairs. But that's a bit different.

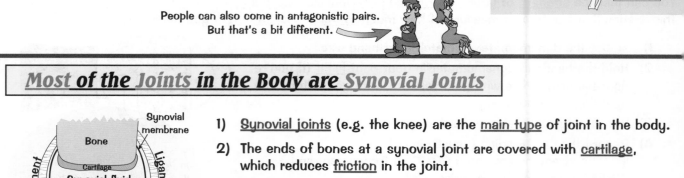

Most of the Joints in the Body are Synovial Joints

Higher

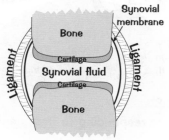

Synovial membrane

Bone

Ligament — Cartilage — Ligament

Synovial fluid

Cartilage

Bone

1) <u>Synovial joints</u> (e.g. the knee) are the <u>main type</u> of joint in the body.

2) The ends of bones at a synovial joint are covered with <u>cartilage</u>, which reduces <u>friction</u> in the joint.

3) The joint is surrounded by a membrane called the <u>synovial membrane</u>.

4) The <u>synovial membrane</u> produces <u>synovial fluid</u> to <u>lubricate</u> the joints, allowing them to move more easily.

Tricepatops — it's an 'armless dinosaur...

Muscles aren't too tricky as long as you remember a couple of <u>key things</u> — they <u>move</u> your <u>bones</u>, and if they're <u>antagonistic</u>, they work in <u>pairs</u>. Try moving your arm just like in these diagrams — you can <u>see</u> the muscles contracting. You might look like a bit of an <u>idiot</u> if people are watching, though.

Joints and Forces

The study of the <u>forces</u> acting on the body is called <u>biomechanics</u>. Fitness practitioners and physiotherapists use biomechanics to help <u>improve</u> the <u>performance</u> of their athletes and to <u>reduce injuries</u>.

A <u>Moment</u> *is a* <u>Turning Force</u>

1) When a <u>force acts</u> on something which has a <u>pivot</u>, it creates a <u>turning</u> or <u>twisting force</u>.

2) A turning or twisting force is also called a <u>moment</u>.

3) You can calculate moments using this equation:

$$\text{Moment} = \text{force} \times \text{perpendicular distance} \quad \text{or} \quad M = F \times r$$

In newton metres (Nm)   In newtons (N)   In metres (m)

The <u>Arm</u> <u>Works as a</u> <u>Lever</u> *so it has a* <u>Moment</u>

1) The <u>arm</u> works as a <u>lever</u> with the <u>elbow</u> as a <u>pivot</u>.

2) This means when a <u>force</u> acts on the arm there's a <u>moment</u>.

3) You can <u>calculate</u> the moment using the equation above.

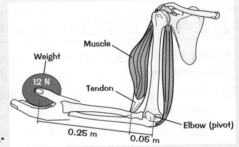

Example: A man is holding a weight, as shown in the diagram. Calculate the moment of the weight.

Answer: The weight is 0.25 + 0.05 = <u>0.30 m</u> away from the pivot (the elbow). The weight is applying a force of <u>12 N</u>.

<u>Moment = Force × Perpendicular Distance</u>, so the moment of the weight is 0.30 × 12 = <u>3.6 Nm</u>.

4) In the example above, the <u>weight</u> is not the only thing applying a force to the arm — the <u>muscle</u> is also applying a force to <u>counteract</u> the <u>moment</u> of the weight and <u>keep the arm still</u>.

5) For the arm to stay still, the <u>moment of the muscle</u> has to be the same as the <u>moment of the weight</u>:

- If the <u>muscle</u> had a <u>bigger moment</u> than the weight, the arm would <u>lift up</u>.
- If the <u>weight</u> had a <u>bigger moment</u> than the muscle, the arm would <u>move down</u>.

6) Because the <u>distance</u> between the muscle and pivot is much <u>smaller</u> than the distance between the weight and pivot, the muscle has to supply a much <u>bigger force</u> to generate the <u>same moment</u>.

7) You can calculate the <u>force</u> applied by the <u>muscle</u> by re-arranging the moment equation.

Following on from the example above:

The weight has a moment of <u>3.6 Nm</u>, so the muscle must also have a moment of <u>3.6 Nm</u>.

The distance between the muscle and the pivot is <u>0.05 m</u>.

Moment = Force × Perpendicular Distance.

This rearranges to: <u>Force = Moment ÷ Perpendicular Distance</u>.

So the Force applied by the muscle is 3.6 ÷ 0.05 = <u>72 N</u>.

Hang on a moment... what?

Moments can be pretty tricky to get your head around but there's a good chance they'll crop up in the exam, so stick with it — you'll be kicking yourself if you give up now and miss out on marks later on.

Injuries and Artificial Joints

You've learnt how joints and muscles normally work, now it's time to see what happens when things go wron

There are Lots of Different Types of Injuries

1) Skeletal-muscular injuries are injuries where your bones, muscles, cartilage, tendons, ligaments or joints get damaged.

2) Here are some of the different types of skeletal-muscular injury:

> Cartilage is the stuff that covers the ends of bones. It stops the bones from rubbing together.

Ligament damage — when a ligament has been stretched or torn, usually because of violent twisting.

Pulled or torn muscles — when a muscle has been torn because it's suddenly over-stretched.

Ruptured tendons — when a tendon breaks, usually because of over-stretching.

Dislocation — when a bone is pulled out of its normal position, again it's twisting that usually does it.

Fractured bones — when a bone breaks because it's put under a lot of stress.

Torn cartilage — when the cartilage around a joint tears due to a sudden impact or violent twisting.

3) If you get one of these injuries you could be treated by a sports physiotherapist.

4) Sports physiotherapists often treat injuries using massaging and manipulation techniques.

5) They may also help put together an exercise programme to help you get fit again once the injury's healed.

If a Joint Can't be Repaired it May be Replaced

If your hip or knee joints get damaged or diseased, they can be replaced with artificial joints. Assuming all goes well, you'll be in less pain and discomfort, and able to walk better. But there are disadvantages...

1) The surrounding tissue may become inflamed and painful — this is caused by the body's reaction to the material the joint is made of.

2) Hip dislocation (ball comes out of its socket) is more common with artificial joints, as are blood clots.

3) There's a risk of infection, as with any surgery.

4) The length of the legs may be slightly different, causing difficulty walking.

5) Artificial joints don't last forever — they usually have to be replaced after 12-15 years.

You Can't Use Any Old Material to Make an Artificial Joint

1) Scientists have to think very carefully about which materials they use to make artificial joints.

2) All artificial joints need to be made from durable materials, otherwise they'll need replacing too often.

3) The material shouldn't react with anything in the body or activate the body's immune system, otherwise it could make the patient ill.

4) The material also needs to be lightweight, so it's not too difficult for patients to move around.

5) Other requirements vary depending on the joint being replaced. For example:
   - If the joint being replaced helps the body carry weight (e.g. the hip joint), the material needs to be strong and sturdy. Metals like titanium are often used to replace this kind of joint.
   - If the joint being replaced requires a lot of movement (e.g. the knee joint), the material needs to be flexible as well as strong. Plastics are often used in this kind of artificial joint.

6) Many modern artificial joints are made from ceramics.

7) Ceramics are smoother than metals and plastics and this helps to reduce the amount of friction in the joint.

What's a skeleton's favourite instrument?... a trom-bone...

Scientists don't only make artificial joints — they can make artificial limbs too. Clever huh?

Energy Needs

You need energy <u>all the time</u>, even when sleeping. How much someone needs depends on the <u>individual</u>.

Different People **Need** Different Amounts **of Energy**

The <u>amount of energy</u> you need depends on your <u>body mass</u> and your level of <u>activity</u>, so the <u>heavier</u> and the <u>more active</u> you are, the <u>more energy</u> you will need.

A LARGER BODY MASS NEEDS MORE ENERGY

Every <u>cell</u> in the body needs <u>energy</u>. So the <u>bigger</u> you are, the <u>more cells</u> you have, and the more energy you'll need. You also need <u>energy</u> to <u>move</u> your body, and it takes <u>more</u> energy to move a <u>bigger mass</u>.

You can work out how much energy you need:

For every <u>kg</u> of <u>body mass</u>, you need <u>5.4 kJ</u> of energy every <u>hour</u>.
This is the <u>basic energy requirement</u> (BER) needed to maintain <u>essential</u> body functions.

> daily basic energy requirement (kJ/day) = 5.4 × 24 hours × body mass (kg)
> E.g. a person weighing 60 kg would require 5.4 × 24 × 60 = 7776 kJ/day

YOU NEED MORE ENERGY IF YOU EXERCISE

The <u>more active</u> you are the <u>more energy</u> you will need.

For example, in half an hour a person who weighs 60 kg will use (on average):

1) 400 kJ <u>walking</u>   2) 750 kJ <u>cycling</u>   3) 1500 kJ <u>running</u>

- An <u>average person</u> needs 8000-13 000 kJ a day.
- <u>Bodybuilders</u> often eat up to 21 000 kJ a day when 'bulking up' for competitions.
- The <u>cyclist</u> Lance Armstrong burnt 25 000-30 000 kJ a day when cycling in the Tour de France.

Body Mass Index **Indicates If You're** <u>Under-</u> **or** <u>Overweight</u>

If you eat <u>more</u> kJs than you <u>use</u> in activity, the <u>excess energy</u> is stored as <u>fat</u> and you gain weight.
If you eat <u>fewer</u> kJs than you <u>use</u> in activity, you <u>use up body fat</u> and <u>lose weight</u>.

The <u>body mass index</u> (BMI) is used as a guide to help decide whether someone is <u>underweight</u>, <u>normal</u>, <u>overweight</u> or <u>obese</u>. It's calculated from their <u>height</u> and <u>weight</u>:

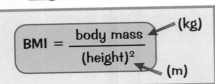

$$BMI = \frac{body\ mass}{(height)^2}\ \text{(kg)}\ \text{(m)}$$

The table shows how BMI is used to <u>classify</u> people's weight.

Body Mass Index	Weight Description
below 18.5	underweight
18.5 - 24.9	normal
25 - 29.9	overweight
30 - 40	moderately obese
above 40	severely obese

BMI isn't always reliable. <u>Weightlifters</u> are likely to be <u>short</u> and have <u>lots of muscle</u>, which weighs more than fat, so they can come out with a <u>high BMI</u> even though they're <u>not overweight</u>.

Nutritionists use <u>BMI</u> and <u>BER</u> calculations to work out how much energy <u>athletes</u> need and advise them on <u>how much</u> they should be eating and <u>what</u> they should be eating.

You use about 300 kJ an hour just sleeping...

Isn't that wonderful to know (but of course, you use up more if you're actually doing something).

Finding the Optimum Diet

To perform at their best, athletes need to be healthy — and that means eating a healthy diet.

Athletes Need Different Diets from Other People

Because athletes push their bodies harder than most of us, they have different dietary requirements:

1) They need plenty of carbohydrates to provide the energy for training and competition.
2) They might need extra protein to build and repair muscle.
3) They need to drink more water to stay hydrated and regulate their body temperature.
4) They need to monitor their fat intake to ensure it stays within healthy limits.

And different types of athletes need different amounts of each thing. For example:

	Carbohydrate (g/day)	Protein (g/day)	Energy (kJ/day)
Average non-athlete	375	70	10 000
Bodybuilder	600	180	17 000
Marathon runner	1000	150	25 000

Sports Nutritionists and Sports Dieticians Study Athletes' Diets

Sports nutritionists and sports dieticians provide nutritional advice to athletes. They work out the best diet for athletes so they can stay healthy and optimise their performance. By studying what the athlete currently eats, they can also work out if they are getting everything they need in the right amounts, and give advice about how to improve their diet.

They may ask the athlete to do a '24-hour dietary recall' or a 'diet diary'.

1) '24-hour dietary recall' — the athlete is asked to write down everything they ate and drank in the last 24 hours. This is a quick easy method for the nutritionist to get an idea of the athlete's eating habits.

2) 'Diet diaries' — the athlete is asked to write down everything they eat and drink for a week or even longer. The nutritionist can examine the diary, work out the athlete's nutrient intake, and provide advice on how to improve the athlete's diet and performance.

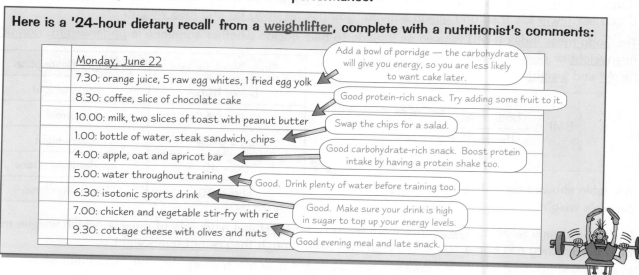

Here is a '24-hour dietary recall' from a weightlifter, complete with a nutritionist's comments:

Monday, June 22

7.30: orange juice, 5 raw egg whites, 1 fried egg yolk — Add a bowl of porridge — the carbohydrate will give you energy, so you are less likely to want cake later.

8.30: coffee, slice of chocolate cake — Good protein-rich snack. Try adding some fruit to it.

10.00: milk, two slices of toast with peanut butter — Swap the chips for a salad.

1.00: bottle of water, steak sandwich, chips — Good carbohydrate-rich snack. Boost protein intake by having a protein shake too.

4.00: apple, oat and apricot bar

5.00: water throughout training — Good. Drink plenty of water before training too.

6.30: isotonic sports drink — Good. Make sure your drink is high in sugar to top up your energy levels.

7.00: chicken and vegetable stir-fry with rice

9.30: cottage cheese with olives and nuts — Good evening meal and late snack.

Dear diet diary, today I have devoured...

Athletes have to be very careful with what they eat every day. So there's no snacking on chocolate, or gorging on ice cream if you've had a bad day, and definitely no pork scratchings.

Energy Rich and Muscle Building Diets

There are a few things athletes can do to improve their performance... and no, I don't mean by taking steroids, or growth hormones, or anything else that's highly illegal — I mean by changing their diet.

Athletes Eat More Carbohydrates Before Competitions

A few days before a competition, endurance athletes (like marathon runners and long-distance cyclists) often increase their intake of complex carbohydrates, e.g. by eating more pasta, bread and rice. This is called 'carbohydrate loading'.

1) Carbohydrates are broken down in the body to release glucose.

2) Excess glucose can be stored in the muscles as a chemical called glycogen.

3) When the muscles need more energy, glycogen is converted back into glucose, which is broken down to release energy (see page 14).

4) 'Carbohydrate loading' increases the amount of glycogen stored in their muscles, so when athletes are running long races, they can run for longer without getting tired.

Carbohydrate loading can have some adverse side effects like muscle stiffness and chest pains — so athletes are advised to only do it a few times a year.

EXAMPLE: TRAINING FOR A LONG-DISTANCE RACE

Nikki has just starting training for the Great North Run®. She's changed her diet to prepare for competition by:

1) Making sure she eats a balanced diet, including lots of fruit and vegetables.

2) Increasing her intake of complex carbohydrates.

3) Eating more snacks — to provide more energy.

4) Making sure she drinks enough water, especially before she goes out training.

Nikki's Daily Diet
8.00: bowl of cereal, banana, cup of tea
11.00: two slices of toast and butter
1.00: pasta with fish and vegetables, fruit, yoghurt
5.00: two slices of bread and butter, banana
6.30: half a litre of water
8.00: potato omelette, fruit
(Water drunk throughout the day.)

Some Athletes Need a High Protein Diet

1) Protein is needed by the body to build and repair muscle.

2) Some athletes, like bodybuilders and powerlifters, eat a high protein diet to help them increase their muscle mass.

3) This involves eating lots of protein-rich foods, like meat, eggs and pulses.

4) They may also drink protein shakes — these are drinks rich in protein that you can buy or make at home. The ingredients can include milk, oats, whey, peanut butter, fish oil and raw eggs.

Information loading — only when exams are on...

This is where a good nutritionist can really come in handy. They know which foods contain the right proportions of the nutrients that you need, and they can tell you where you're going wrong. It's like my mum always says — you only get out as good as you put in...

Sports Drinks

Imagine you've just run a marathon. You're exhausted and thirsty. You reach for a water bottle...
Think again, and swap the water for an isotonic sports drink. Here's why.

During Exercise You Lose Water, Glucose and Electrolytes

During exercise your body respires more. This means:

1) You use up a lot of glucose by breaking it down to release energy.

2) You get warmer — which means you sweat to cool down.

3) Sweat contains lots of water and ions called electrolytes — so you're losing these from your body.

After exercise you need to replenish your body's supplies.

Electrolytes in a litre of sweat (on average):	
0.02 g	calcium
0.05 g	magnesium
1.15 g	sodium
0.23 g	potassium
1.48 g	chloride

Isotonic Drinks Contain Water, Glucose and Electrolytes

1) Isotonic sports drinks are designed to help athletes recover after exercise.

2) They contain water, glucose and electrolytes in the same concentrations as they are in the body.

3) So they replace the water and electrolytes lost during sweating, and top up carbohydrate stores.

Many athletes use isotonic sports drinks to rehydrate after strenuous training and competition.
Several brands of isotonic sports drinks are available to buy.

> WARNING: Because isotonic sports drinks contain high levels of glucose (a sugar), they are bad for your teeth and can cause weight gain if used by non-athletes. Sports drinks should only be used if you train to a fairly high level (3 – 5 times a week for 45 – 90 minutes).

Sports drinks are different from energy drinks — energy drinks just contain lots of sugar (and often caffeine

Isotonic Drinks Rehydrate You Better Than Water

Drinking an isotonic sports drink is better than drinking water if you are dehydrated because:

1) Drinking water can make you bloated and suppress your thirst — this can put you off drinking enough to replace your losses.

2) If you don't have enough ions in your blood, you struggle to retain the water you drink — it takes a lot longer to be absorbed. Because isotonic drinks replace the ions lost during exercise, your body can retain the water in the drink.

3) Isotonic drinks replace the electrolytes you have lost, as well as replacing the water.

You Can Get Hypertonic and Hypotonic Drinks too

1) As well as isotonic drinks, you can also get hypertonic drinks and hypotonic drinks.

2) These all contain water and electrolytes but the amount of glucose they contain is different.

3) Hypertonic drinks contain more glucose than isotonic drinks — they can be used to supplement the body's daily carbohydrate intake and give you loads of energy.

4) Hypotonic drinks contain less glucose than isotonic drinks — they can be used to quickly replace fluids that have been lost due to sweating but they don't contain lots of calories.

Ice 'n' tonic — I prefer my gin neat...

So not only do isotonic drinks give you bags of energy, they're better at replacing water than water is — who'd have thought it. Plus they always come in really good flavours — it's enough to make anybody want to train three to five times a week for 45 - 90 minutes.

Revision Summary for Section 2

That wasn't such a bad section. Now you know a bit about how the human body works and the people and techniques used to keep it healthy... you could almost be a healthcare scientist (well, maybe after A-levels and then three years at Uni, but let's not dwell on details). Here are a few questions to check that you know it...

1) Name and describe the role of two professions involved in healthcare or fitness.

2) Name the three types of blood vessel and describe how each one is designed for its function.

3) What organ pumps blood around the body?

4) Outline the movement of blood around the cardiovascular system.

5) What do the valves in the heart do?

6) What is the thorax?

7) Put the following parts of the thorax into the correct order (from the mouth to the lungs):
a) alveoli, b) trachea, c) bronchioles, d) bronchi.

8) Describe what happens to cause you to: a) breathe in, b) breathe out.

9) What would a respiratory physiologist use to measure lung capacity?

10) What do the following terms mean? a) tidal volume, b) vital capacity.

11) How would you measure someone's breathing rate?

12) How does exercising affect a person's breathing rate?

13) What effect does exercise have on a person's tidal volume?

14) What is respiration?

15) What is the difference between aerobic and anaerobic respiration? Give the word equation for each.

16) Why does an 'oxygen debt' develop in muscles that are respiring anaerobically?

17) How would you measure someone's heart rate?

18) How does exercising affect a person's heart rate?

19) Describe how you could monitor recovery time.

20) How does the body reduce its temperature when it's too hot?

21) How does the body increase its temperature when it's too cold?

22) Give three ways in which we lose water.

23) Describe how insulin controls blood sugar levels.

24) Describe how glucagon controls blood sugar levels.

25) Describe how you could measure the glucose level in: a) urine, b) blood.

26) How could you measure muscle strength?

27) Describe the relationship between ligaments, tendons, muscles and bones.

28) Describe what antagonistic muscles are, using the biceps and triceps as an example.

29) In a synovial joint, what does synovial fluid do and what produces it?

30) What is a moment and what equation would you use to calculate one?

31) Give one disadvantage of having an artificial hip.

32) Give two properties that a material must have for it to be used to make an artificial joint.

33)*What is the daily basic energy requirement for a person weighing 75 kg?

34) What is the formula for calculating body mass index?

35)*Cecil is 180 cm tall and weighs 85 kg. Calculate his BMI.

36) If a person's BMI is 21 are they underweight, normal, overweight, moderately obese or severely obese?

37) Why do the dietary requirements for athletes differ from those for most of us?

38) What is a '24-hour dietary recall'?

39) What is 'carbohydrate loading'?

40) What do isotonic drinks contain and why do they rehydrate you better than water?

41) What are hypertonic and hypotonic drinks used for?

* Answers on page 92.

Section 2 — Health, Exercise and Nutrition

Product Standards

This section's mostly about the <u>properties</u> of different <u>materials</u> and how to pick the <u>best material</u> for a job. Making things isn't just about starting with the right materials though — you also need to be sure that your product's going to do what it's supposed to (and do it <u>safely</u>). That's where <u>product standards</u> come in...

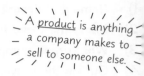

Products Need to be <u>Safe</u> — and <u>Work Properly</u> Too

A <u>product</u> is anything a company makes to sell to someone else.

1) You'd be cross if a product didn't do its <u>job</u> properly, or <u>broke</u> after a few days.

2) A badly made product might also be <u>dangerous</u>.

3) That's why it's important for products to meet certain basic <u>standards</u>.

4) All new products are tested to make sure they are <u>fit for purpose</u>. This means checking that the product <u>does</u> the job it <u>claims</u> to do. (E.g. if you bought a raincoat and it let water in when you wore it, it wouldn't be fit for purpose.)

5) New products are also tested for <u>quality</u>. This means checking that the product is <u>safe</u> and <u>reliable</u>. (E.g. if you bought a phone and it broke the next day, it would be poor quality.)

Some Organisations Help to <u>Promote Good Standards</u>

Here are a couple of examples of organisations that help to ensure <u>good product standards</u>:

The <u>British Standards Institution</u>

1) The <u>British Standards Institution</u> (BSI) produces <u>standards</u> labelled with '<u>BS</u>' and a number.

2) Each standard is a document describing how well a product should do its job, how safe it should be, etc.

 This is the <u>BSI Kitemark</u>®. If a product displays this <u>logo</u>, then it has been tested by the BSI to make sure it <u>conforms</u> to the BSI standards the manufacturer says it does.

The <u>European Committee for Standardisation</u>

1) A wide <u>variety</u> of different <u>products</u> have to meet certain <u>legal requirements</u> (<u>safety</u> standards), before they can be sold in the <u>European Community</u>.

2) This includes products <u>made</u> in Europe and products <u>imported</u> into Europe.

The standards that the products have to meet are set by the <u>European Committee for Standardisation</u>. Products which meet these standards carry a '<u>CE mark</u>'. The CE mark is a logo which looks like this:

It's your job to enforce good standards — of revision...

Have a look around your house for stuff that has the <u>CE mark</u> on. You'll be surprised how many things have to meet the standards set by the <u>European Committee for Standardisation</u> before they can be sold. Products that need to carry the CE mark include toys, safety equipment, medical equipment, electrical items... the list goes on

Mechanical Properties

Materials <u>scientists</u> research the properties of different materials and help <u>manufacturers</u> to decide what <u>materials</u> would be best to use in their <u>products</u>. This page is about some of the <u>properties</u> they study...

Materials **Can Have** *Compressive* **or** *Tensile* **Strength**

1) You can apply a <u>compressive force</u> or a <u>tensile force</u> to an object.

<u>COMPRESSION</u> means that the object is being <u>crushed</u> or <u>squashed</u>. This bottle is under <u>compression</u>.

<u>TENSION</u> means that the object is being <u>stretched</u>. This rope is under <u>tension</u>.

2) One part of an object can be under <u>tension</u> while another part is under <u>compression</u>. For example, look at this bow and arrow:

The outside of the bow is under <u>tension</u> (it's being <u>stretched</u>).

The inside of the bow is under <u>compression</u> (it's being <u>squashed</u>).

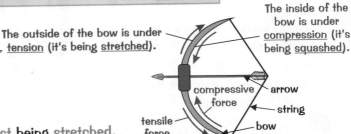

compressive force · arrow · string · bow · tensile force

3) Materials that have a high <u>compressive strength</u> can <u>resist</u> being <u>crushed</u> or <u>squashed</u>.

4) Materials that have a high <u>tensile strength</u> can <u>resist</u> being <u>stretched</u>.

To *Describe Materials Usefully* **You Need to** *Use the Right Words*

STIFFNESS / FLEXIBILITY

If a material doesn't <u>deform</u> (change shape) much when you apply a force then it's <u>stiff</u>. If it <u>changes shape</u> easily it's <u>flexible</u>. Something can be made more <u>rigid</u> (stiffer) by using a different, stiffer material or by changing its shape (making it thicker, say).

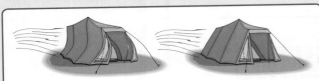

Using stiffer poles makes a tent more rigid.

TOUGHNESS / BRITTLENESS

A <u>tough</u> material can <u>deform</u> quite a lot without breaking. A <u>brittle</u> material <u>breaks</u> before it deforms very much at all.

If you <u>sit on</u> a pair of glasses made from a <u>tough</u> material, they can (in theory) be bent back into shape afterwards. If the material is <u>brittle</u> though, they'll just <u>break</u>. Oops.

HARDNESS

A <u>hard</u> material is resistant to <u>scratching</u> or <u>indentation</u>. A <u>harder</u> material will be able to <u>cut through</u> a <u>softer</u> one.

Chisels are made out of <u>hard</u> material so that they can cut easily through softer materials like wood.

DENSITY

A <u>dense</u> material has a <u>large mass</u> contained in a <u>small volume</u>. Most sports equipment is made from materials of low density, since you usually want it to be as <u>light</u> as possible.

You need a racing bike to be <u>big enough</u> for you but as <u>light as possible</u> (so you can go as fast as possible). Similarly, you'd want a lightweight tennis racquet — it'd take a lot more effort to swing something really heavy.

Sometimes it's useful for materials to be stiff and hard...

It's important that you use the <u>right words</u> to describe the properties of materials. It's easy to get confused, so make sure you know what's meant by <u>stiff</u>, <u>flexible</u>, <u>tough</u>, <u>brittle</u>, <u>hard</u> and <u>dense</u>...

Measuring Mechanical Properties

A <u>materials scientist</u> needs to know how to <u>test</u> all the properties on page 25 too — and so do you...

You Can Compare the Stiffness of Different Materials

1) To compare the <u>stiffness</u> (see page 25) of different materials, this is what you'd do:

2) Remember to wear <u>safety specs</u> and to keep your <u>feet</u> well away from the hanging loads.

3) Gradually increase the <u>load</u> (or <u>force</u>) on the material by adding weights, and measure the <u>extension</u> (total length – original length) of the material each time using a <u>ruler</u>, as shown on the right.

4) You can then compare the stiffness of different materials in <u>two</u> ways:

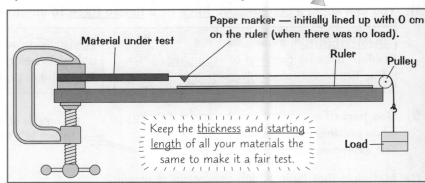

Paper marker — initially lined up with 0 cm on the ruler (when there was no load).

Material under test

Ruler

Pulley

Load

Keep the <u>thickness</u> and <u>starting length</u> of all your materials the same to make it a fair test.

① **PLOT A FORCE-EXTENSION GRAPH**

Plot a graph with <u>force</u> on the <u>x-axis</u> and <u>extension</u> on the <u>y-axis</u>. E.g. this graph shows the results of testing three different materials with increasingly heavy loads. The <u>stiffest</u> material is shown by the <u>shallowest gradient</u>.

extension (mm)

stiffest material

force (N)

② **CALCULATE THE STIFFNESS CONSTANT**

This is Hooke's law: | Force (N) = Constant (N/cm) × Extension (cm)

You can <u>calculate</u> the <u>stiffness constant</u> for a material by re-arranging the equation:

Constant (N/cm) = Force (N) ÷ Extension (cm)

The <u>larger</u> the <u>constant</u>, the <u>stiffer</u> the material.

Force is measured in newtons (N).

Materials with small stiffness constants are flexible (see p. 25).

You Can Measure the Strength of a Material

1) To find a material's <u>TENSILE STRENGTH</u> you could use the same apparatus as for measuring stiffness (shown in the diagram above). You just keep on <u>adding the loads</u> until the material <u>breaks</u>.

2) The load at which the object breaks is its <u>tensile strength</u>.

3) To measure <u>COMPRESSIVE STRENGTH</u> you could use the apparatus in this diagram. You'd keep <u>tightening the clamp</u> until the object <u>broke</u>.

4) The load at which the object breaks is its <u>compressive strength</u>.

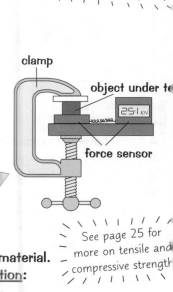

clamp

object under te

25·1 KN

force sensor

See page 25 for more on tensile and compressive strength

| Stress: | 1) <u>Stress</u> is the <u>amount of pressure</u> that is being put on a bit of material. You can find the stress on a piece of material using this <u>equation</u>:

Stress (N/cm²) = Force (N) ÷ Cross-sectional Area (cm²) ⟵ Of the bit of material.

2) The <u>greater</u> the <u>stress</u> needed to break a material, the <u>stronger</u> the material is.

And the compressive strength of my finger is — ouch...

Being able to <u>test the strength</u> of materials is really important — you wouldn't want, say, part of an aeroplane engine to <u>snap</u> in half right in the middle of a flight because it wasn't made of a strong enough material...

Measuring Mechanical Properties

Here are some more <u>tests</u> that you need to know about. They're important so try and stay awake.

Density <u>is</u> Mass Divided by Volume

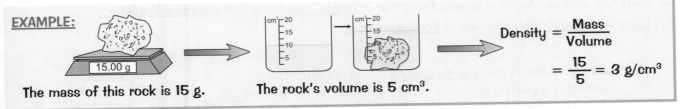

1) <u>Density</u> is a measure of how <u>heavy</u> a material is for its <u>size</u>.
2) You can calculate the <u>density</u> of a material using this <u>equation</u>:
3) You can find the <u>mass</u> of a piece of material by <u>weighing</u> it using a <u>mass balance</u>.
4) You can find the <u>volume</u> of a piece of material by putting it in <u>water</u> and measuring how much the water level <u>rises</u>.

$$\text{Density (g/cm}^3) = \frac{\text{Mass (g)}}{\text{Volume (cm}^3)}$$

EXAMPLE:

The mass of this rock is 15 g.   The rock's volume is 5 cm³.

$$\text{Density} = \frac{\text{Mass}}{\text{Volume}}$$
$$= \frac{15}{5} = 3 \text{ g/cm}^3$$

You Can Compare the Hardness of Different Materials by Denting Them

1) To compare the <u>hardness</u> of different materials you'll need the equipment shown in this diagram:
2) Drop the <u>weight</u> down the tube.
3) The weight will hit the <u>nail</u> and <u>push</u> it into the <u>material</u> you're testing.
4) Measure the <u>depth</u> of the dent made in each material.
5) The <u>hardest</u> material will be the one with the <u>smallest</u> dent.

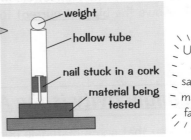

weight
hollow tube
nail stuck in a cork
material being tested

Use the same weight dropped from the same height for each material to make it a fair test (see p. 85).

Impact Tests Can be Used to Compare Toughness

1) To compare the <u>toughness</u> of different materials you'll need the equipment shown in this diagram:
2) Put a <u>deep groove</u> in each material to be tested.
3) <u>Break</u> the materials one at a time by swinging a <u>pendulum hammer</u> from a <u>set</u> height. Measure <u>how high</u> the pendulum hammer swings after each material is <u>broken</u>.
4) <u>Tough</u> materials <u>absorb more energy</u> when they <u>break</u> than <u>brittle</u> materials. This means the pendulum will have <u>less</u> energy after breaking the material and it <u>won't swing as high</u>.
5) The <u>toughest</u> material will be the one where the pendulum swings the <u>least distance</u> after the material breaks.

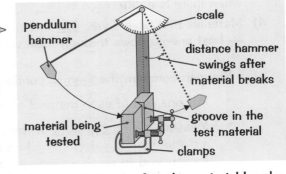

pendulum hammer
scale
distance hammer swings after material breaks
material being tested
groove in the test material
clamps

You Can Test a Material for Corrosion by Leaving it in Air or Water

1) <u>Corrosion</u> is when a material <u>reacts</u> with things in its <u>environment</u> (like oxygen or water) and gradually <u>breaks down</u> (e.g. rust is a type of corrosion).
2) When a material <u>corrodes</u>, its properties (e.g. density, hardness, strength etc.) change.
3) To test whether a material will <u>corrode</u> or not you can leave it in <u>air</u> or <u>water</u> for a fixed amount of time.
4) If after that time, the material's properties <u>haven't</u> changed much, it's said to be <u>resistant</u> to corrosion.

I'm not dense... I know all of these tests...

There's <u>a lot</u> to learn on this page but stick with it — you never know when you'll need to test some <u>properties</u>.

Measuring Electrical and Thermal Properties

The last few pages were all about the <u>mechanical</u> properties of materials. Now it's time to have a sneaky peak at the <u>electrical</u> and <u>thermal</u> properties of materials and how they can be measured.

Electrical Conductivity is the Ability to Conduct Electricity

1) Materials with a <u>high electrical conductivity</u> conduct electricity very <u>well</u> — a large electrical <u>current</u> can flow through them for a given <u>voltage</u>.

2) For example, <u>gold</u> and <u>copper</u> have a very <u>high electrical conductivity</u>.

3) Materials with a <u>low</u> electrical conductivity <u>don't</u> conduct electricity very well.

4) Materials with an electrical conductivity that is <u>nearly zero</u> are called <u>electrical insulators</u>.

5) <u>Glass</u> and <u>plastic</u> are examples of <u>good insulators</u>.

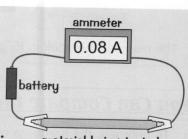

- You can compare the <u>electrical</u> conductivity of different materials by putting a piece of each material (one at a time) into a <u>circuit</u> along with an <u>ammeter</u>.

- The ammeter measures the <u>current</u> flowing through the circuit.

- The material with the <u>highest electrical conductivity</u> will be the one which allows the <u>biggest current</u> to flow when it is put in the circuit.

ammeter
0.08 A
battery
material being tested

Thermal Conductivity is the Ability to Conduct Heat Energy

1) In the same way that some materials conduct <u>electricity</u> better than others, certain materials also conduct <u>heat</u> better than others.

2) The ability to conduct heat energy is called <u>thermal conductivity</u>.

3) Materials with a <u>high</u> thermal conductivity (e.g. <u>metals</u>) conduct heat energy very quickly when there is a difference in <u>temperature</u> between one side of the material and the other.

4) Materials that have a very <u>low</u> thermal conductivity (e.g. <u>air</u>) are called <u>thermal insulators</u> — heat energy flows through them very slowly.

You can compare the <u>thermal</u> conductivity of different materials using this experiment:

- Put one end of each material above a Bunsen burner <u>flame</u>.

- Measure the <u>temperature</u> of the other end using a <u>digital thermometer</u>. <u>Time</u> how long it takes for this end to reach a particular temperature.

- The material with the <u>highest thermal conductivity</u> will be the one which takes the <u>least</u> amount of time for the other end to reach that temperature.

- Make sure that all the materials start at the <u>same temperature</u> — otherwise it won't be a <u>fair test</u>.

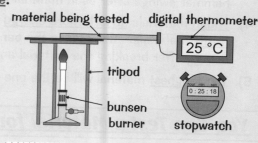

material being tested   digital thermometer
25 °C
tripod
bunsen burner
stopwatch

See page 85 for more on fair tests.

Conducting electricity — I've never heard of that orchestra...

Materials with high <u>electrical conductivity</u> are useful if you're making <u>electrical gizmos</u> — it'd be no good having wires made out of plastic. Materials with high <u>thermal conductivity</u> can be pretty useful too. They're used to make things like <u>pans</u> — it'd take a long time to cook your beans if the pan was made out of an insulator.

Ceramics

OK, so you already know that <u>different materials</u> have <u>different properties</u>. Well, you also need to know the typical properties of some common materials and what they're used for. First up — <u>ceramics</u>.

Ceramics are Hard but Break Easily

Ceramics have a number of <u>common features</u>:

1) They're very <u>hard</u>.

2) They break when <u>bent</u> — they're <u>brittle</u>, not flexible.

3) They're <u>poor conductors</u> of <u>heat</u> — they have <u>low thermal conductivity</u>.

4) They have very <u>high melting points</u>.

5) They <u>won't react</u> with many chemicals — they're <u>resistant</u> to <u>chemical attack</u>.

Ceramics are Useful for Lots of Things:

SPACE SHUTTLES

When a <u>space shuttle</u> re-enters the Earth's atmosphere, the shuttle can reach temperatures of up to <u>1650 °C</u> (that's very, very hot). The shuttle is protected from these temperatures by being covered in <u>heat-resistant tiles</u>, which are made from <u>ceramics</u>. Ceramics are a good material to use because:

1) They have a <u>low thermal conductivity</u>. This stops the inside of the shuttle from becoming dangerously hot.

2) They have a <u>high melting point</u> — if the tiles started to melt they'd be <u>useless</u> for protecting the space shuttle.

CATALYTIC CONVERTERS

1) Catalytic converters are used in modern <u>cars</u> to <u>remove</u> some of the <u>harmful gases</u> that come out of the <u>exhaust</u>.

2) The <u>temperature</u> a catalytic converter works at is around <u>350-400 °C</u>.

3) Catalytic converters contain a <u>honeycomb</u> structure <u>coated</u> in a thin layer of a <u>metal catalyst</u>.

4) The honeycomb structure is made from <u>ceramics</u>. This is because ceramics have <u>high melting points</u>, so they won't be <u>damaged</u> by the high temperatures.

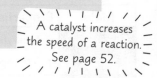

A catalyst increases the speed of a reaction. See page 52.

ARTIFICIAL JOINTS

Ceramics are used to make some <u>artificial joints</u> (see page 18). They are a good material to use for this because:

1) They are <u>resistant to chemical attack</u>, so they won't <u>react</u> with anything in the body.

2) They're also <u>hard</u> and <u>durable</u>, so they won't need <u>replacing</u> too often.

3) Ceramics are <u>smooth</u>. This reduces the amount of <u>friction</u> (rubbing) at the joint.

r Amic Tiles — protecting space shuttles since 1981...

there you have it. Ceramics are used for making much more than just bowls, mugs and novelty hippos. But don't learn the <u>uses</u> of ceramics — you need to know <u>why</u> their properties make them <u>suitable</u> for these uses too.

Metals

Metals are used for all sorts of things — because they have some really <u>useful properties</u>.

The <u>Properties</u> of Metals <u>are Due to Their</u> Bonding

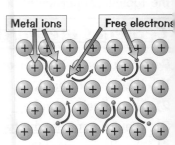

1) The atoms in metals are held together by <u>metallic bonds</u>.
2) These bonds allow the <u>outer electron(s)</u> of each atom to move freely.
3) This creates a '<u>sea</u>' of free <u>electrons</u> that can move throughout the metal.
4) There is a very <u>strong attraction</u> between the <u>positive</u> metal ions and the <u>negative</u> free electrons.

Metals are <u>Strong</u> but <u>Flexible</u>

Not all metals have exactly the <u>same</u> properties, but in <u>general</u>:

1) They have a <u>high tensile strength</u> (see page 25) — this is because the metallic bonds holding the atoms together are strong and difficult to break.
2) They have a <u>high thermal conductivity</u> (see page 28) — this is because the free electrons can move and carry heat energy through the metal.
3) They're <u>flexible</u> (can be bent) and <u>malleable</u> (can be hammered into shape and rolled into sheets). This is because the atoms in the metal are arranged in <u>layers</u> which can slide over one another.

<u>Alloys</u> are Harder <u>Than</u> Pure Metals

1) An <u>alloy</u> is a mixture of <u>two or more</u> elements. At least one of these elements must be a <u>metal</u>.
2) Different elements have <u>different sized atoms</u>. When another element is added to a pure metal it will upset the <u>layers</u> of metal atoms, making it more <u>difficult</u> for them to <u>slide</u> over each other.
3) This means that alloys tend to be <u>harder</u> than pure metals.

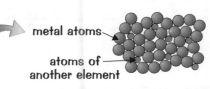

metal atoms

atoms of another element

A Metal's <u>Exact Properties</u> <u>Decide How It's Best</u> Used

The properties above are <u>typical properties</u> of metals. But different metals and alloys have their own <u>specific properties</u> too. It's these specific properties that make them suitable for <u>different uses</u>.

Metal	Properties	Good for making things that...
Aluminium alloys	• Low density (lightweight) • Strong	...need to be strong but lightweight. E.g. aircraft frames, bicycle frames, tennis racquets.
Stainless Steel	• Corrosion resistant (won't rust)	...could get wet but you need not to go rusty. E.g. car parts (exhausts, trims and grills), golf clubs, ship containers, road tankers, chemical tankers, parts of MRI scanners, surgical instruments and surgical implants.
Titanium and its alloys	• Very strong • Low density • Corrosion resistant	...need to be strong, lightweight and don't rust. E.g. high-performance bicycle frames, aircraft frames, replacement hip joints (see page 18).

<u>Daniel Craig — he's definitely a strong Bond...</u>

It's not just the main structure of an aeroplane that's made of aluminium — parts of the <u>engines</u>, the <u>seat support</u> and even the cabin crew's <u>trolleys</u> are all made of aluminium. All this aluminium means the plane's light enough to fl

Polymers

Polymers are just loads of little molecules <u>joined together</u> in big, long <u>chains</u>.
All <u>plastics</u> are polymers — so they're pretty important materials as modern materials go...

The Properties of Polymers are Due to Their Structure

1) <u>Polymers</u> are made up of <u>atoms</u> which are joined together to form <u>long chains</u>.

2) Lots of these long chains can then pack together <u>side by side</u>.

3) The <u>atoms</u> in the chains are held together by <u>strong covalent bonds</u>.

4) The <u>chains</u> are held together by <u>weaker</u> forces of attraction.

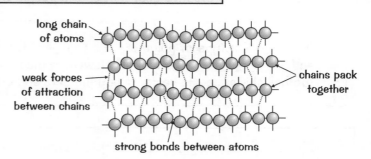

Polymers Have Some Characteristic Properties...

Because they have similar structures, most polymers share certain <u>properties</u>:

1) They are <u>flexible</u> — this is because the bonds between the chains are weak, so the chains can easily slide across one another as the polymer bends.

2) They have <u>low thermal conductivity</u> (see page 28) — this is because the chains tend to be packed together loosely, so heat energy is transferred slowly through the polymer.

3) They have a <u>low density</u> — this is because the chains in many polymers have branches coming off them, so they can't pack together very tightly.

<u>Density</u> is how heavy something is for its size — see page 25 for more.

You Can Get Thermoplastic and Thermosetting Polymers

The strength of the <u>forces of attraction</u> between the <u>chains</u> of a polymer affect the polymer's properties. For example:

THERMOPLASTIC POLYMERS (e.g. polyethene) have very <u>weak</u> forces of attraction between the chains, which are <u>easy</u> to overcome. As a result the polymer is <u>flexible</u> and easy to <u>melt</u>. When it <u>cools</u>, the polymer sets into a new shape. You can melt these polymers and <u>remould</u> them as many times as you like.

THERMOSETTING POLYMERS have strong cross-links (covalent bonds) between the chains. These hold the chains together in a <u>solid structure</u>. As a result the polymer <u>doesn't soften</u> when it's heated and it <u>can't be remoulded</u>.

The <u>strength</u> of the forces of attraction between the chains of a polymer is also affected by:

1) The <u>LENGTH</u> of the chains — long chains are held together more strongly than shorter chains.

2) The amount of <u>BRANCHING</u> in the polymer — chains with fewer <u>branches</u> can <u>pack together</u> more closely. This increases the strength of the forces of attraction between them.

In general, polymers with <u>stronger</u> forces of attraction between the chains are <u>stronger</u>, <u>denser</u> and have a <u>higher melting point</u> than polymers with <u>weaker</u> forces between the chains.

Higher

oose your polymers wisely...

really important for scientists to understand the <u>properties</u> of a material when they're <u>designing</u> things — you
uldn't want them to use a <u>rigid polymer</u> to make your supermarket carrier bags. Make sure you've got your
d round the main properties of polymers — there's plenty of examples of what they're used for coming up...

Polymers

OK, so you've seen why polymers have the properties that they do — now here's why they're useful.

Polymers Are Used to Make Sports Equipment

Lots of the clothes and protective gear that sports people wear are made out of polymers:

1) Polyester is a type of polymer. It's lightweight, durable (hardwearing) and water-resistant. Lots of sportswear is made of polyester — including football shirts, sports vests, fleecy jumpers and outdoor jackets.

2) Elastane (LYCRA®) is another type of polymer. It has excellent elasticity, it's lightweight, durable and resistant to water (and sweat). Sportswear which needs to be stretchy for comfort and fit is often made with elastane — for example swimwear, wetsuits, cycle shorts, athletic and aerobic clothing.

3) Crash helmets need to be strong, lightweight, and flexible. The hard outer casing is made from a strong polymer and the inner lining is usually made from polystyrene foam, which is flexible and crushes on impact.

Kevlar® is Used to Make Tennis Racquets and Golf Clubs

Kevlar® is a polymer that's used to make:

TENNIS RACQUETS

Some tennis racquets have strings made from Kevlar®. Kevlar® strings are light, flexible and very strong. They can absorb a lot of energy when the racquet hits a ball without breaking.

Kevlar® is also used to make bulletproof vests.

GOLF CLUBS

Kevlar® is added to the shaft (handle) of some golf clubs. Kevlar® is light and when the golf club is used to hit a golf ball, it can absorb large amounts of energy without breaking. It gives the golf club strength without making it too heavy to swing.

Who needs Olly Murs when you've got poly-mers?

It's a good job polymers were invented — without them we'd have rubbish cycle helmets, tennis racquets and golf clubs. And sportswear wouldn't be nearly so comfy and hardwearing as it is. So remember — it's materials scientists you need to ~~blame~~ thank for your (pretty much) indestructible, and no doubt incredibly stylish, P.E. k

Composites

Composites are great, taking the good points of two different materials — it's a bit like a woolly jumper if you think about it — it keeps you warm and is really handy as a goal post but it doesn't eat grass all day.

Composites are Made of Two or More Different Materials

Composites are a mixture of two or more materials. The properties of a composite depend on the properties of the materials it is made from. For example:

1) Wood-plastic composites are made from wood and plastic. They behave like wood, and can be shaped using woodworking tools — but are water-resistant (like plastic).

2) Cermet is made from ceramic and metal. It's durable and heat-resistant (like ceramic), but malleable (like metal).

3) Carbon Fibre (or Carbon Fibre Reinforced Plastic — CRP) is made by mixing a plastic with fibres made of carbon. It has a low density (like plastic) but is very strong (like carbon).

4) Fibreglass (or Glass Reinforced Plastic — GRP) is made from a plastic and fibres made of glass. It has a low density (like plastic) but is very strong (like glass).

Composite Materials Have Loads of Uses

Laminated Windscreens are Made From Glass and Plastic

1) Modern vehicles have laminated windscreens.

2) These windscreens are made from two layers of glass with a layer of plastic (a polymer) in between.

3) They're a lot safer than windscreens made with just glass.

4) This is because, if the windscreen breaks, the plastic will hold the glass shards together (so you're less likely to be hit by flying glass).

Some Sports Materials are Made Using Carbon Fibre

Because carbon fibre is so strong and light, it's used in loads of sporting equipment. For example:

 Bike frames — CRP is much lighter than traditional materials like aluminium or steel.

 Racquet frames — CRP is strong enough to hold the strings in tension, and lightweight enough for easy handling.

 Yachts — CRP is strong and lightweight, so it's used to make some very speedy yachts.

Golf clubs also need to be strong and lightweight, so many of them contain some CRP too.

Racing Car Brakes are Made Using Ceramics and Carbon

1) When a car brakes, there's friction between the brake pads and the brake discs. This friction makes the discs and pads very hot.

2) Brake discs need to have a high melting point — if the discs started to melt they'd be useless for stopping the car.

3) The discs must also be durable so they don't wear down too quickly.

4) The high melting point and hardness of ceramics makes them ideal for the discs and pads.

5) Mixing the ceramics with carbon makes the brakes lighter, which helps the car go faster.

rbon fibre — it's CRP...

bon fibre comes in pretty handy because it's so strong and light. The problem is, it's also pretty pricey — 'd be lucky to get a carbon-fibre bike for less than a grand (and I dread to think how much CRP yachts cost).

Choosing the Best Material

The last few pages have been all about the different types of materials and their properties. Now it's time to bring all that together and see how scientists choose between different materials. There are lots of decisions to make — e.g. should the material be natural or synthetic and what properties does it need to have.

Materials Can be Natural or Synthetic

1) Natural materials are found naturally in the environment (e.g. wood, wool, silk, metals).

2) Synthetic materials are not found naturally — we have to make them ourselves (e.g. plastics like polyethene, synthetic fabrics like polyester).

3) There are advantages and disadvantages to using synthetic materials:

Advantages	Disadvantages
Synthetic materials are often cheaper than natural materials.	Many synthetic materials come from unsustainable sources (e.g. crude oil).
Synthetic materials can be more durable (last longer) than natural materials.	
You can change the properties of a synthetic material to match what you need the material for.	Many synthetic materials are not biodegradable and so are difficult to dispose of.
You can make a synthetic material in whatever shape or size that you need.	

Things that are biodegradable will break down naturally.

You Can Choose Materials Based on Their Properties

1) The material an object is made from is chosen based on how its properties make it suitable for the job.

Materials with a low thermal conductivity are used to keep things hot or cold.

Low-density materials are used to make objects that need to be light.

Flexible materials are used to make things that need to bend and stretch.

Shock-absorbing materials are used to make things that need to withstand big forces.

Smooth materials are used to reduce friction.

Materials with a high tensile strength are used to provide support or carry loads.

Example: Imagine that you wanted to make a wetsuit for scuba diving. What properties does the wetsuit material need?

Answer: The material should be flexible to allow for comfortable movement. It needs low thermal conductivity (to give enough insulation to keep the diver warm).

2) The materials used to make a certain product often change over time.

3) This could be because a new material has been created which is more suited for that particular purpose. (E.g. tennis racquets used to be made from wood, but today they're made from carbon fibre.)

4) Or it could be because cheaper materials with similar properties have become available.

Pick me — pick me — pick me...

In an exam, if you're asked to say which would be the best material for a job, don't panic — just use your own knowledge and any information that you're given in the question to decide what material is most suitable.

Revision Summary for Section 3

You really shouldn't skip these questions. What's the point in reading that great big section if you're not going to check whether you really know it all? When it comes to the exam, you'll be glad you did.

1) Give the names of two organisations that set product standards.
2) What do the terms compression and tension mean?
3) What word is used to describe a material that can deform quite a lot without breaking.
4)* Which material, A, B or C, shown on the force-extension graph is the stiffest?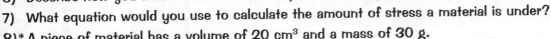
5) What equation would you use to calculate the stiffness constant of a material?
6) Describe how you would measure the compressive strength of a material.
7) What equation would you use to calculate the amount of stress a material is under?
8)* A piece of material has a volume of 20 cm³ and a mass of 30 g.
   Calculate the density of the material.
9) Describe how you would compare the hardness of two materials.
10) What is corrosion?
11) Describe how you would compare the electrical conductivity of two materials.
12) Define the term thermal conductivity.
13) List three properties of ceramics.
14) a) Give two reasons why heat-resistant tiles on space shuttles are made using ceramic materials.
    b) Suggest one other use of ceramic materials.
15) Give two properties of metals. Explain these properties in terms of the structure of a metal.
16) What is an alloy?
17) Name two common uses of aluminium alloys.
18) Give two properties of titanium that make it suitable for building bicycle frames.
19) Describe the structure of a polymer.
20) Explain why some polymers have: a) low thermal conductivity,
                                     b) low density.
21) Explain the difference between thermoplastic polymers and thermosetting polymers.
22) Describe how increasing the chain length would affect the strength of the forces of attraction
    between two polymer chains.
23) Why do crash helmets usually have an inner lining made from polystyrene foam?
24) Explain why Kevlar® is added to the shafts of golf clubs.
25) What is a composite material? Give an example of a composite material.
26) Suggest why laminated windscreens are used in cars rather than windscreens made with just glass.
27) Name two pieces of sports equipment that are made using carbon fibre.
28) Explain how the properties of carbon-ceramic composites make them suitable for
    use as racing car brakes.
29) What's the difference between a natural material and a synthetic material?
30) Give two advantages and two disadvantages of using synthetic materials rather than natural materials.
31) Suggest one reason why a material used to make a certain product may change over time.

* Answers on page 92.

Section 3 — Materials and Their Properties

Agricultural and Food Scientists

The population of the world is increasing every day. We need to make sure that there are enough food resources to support this increase. This is where agricultural scientists step in. These are scientists who study plants and animals to try and increase and improve food production.

Agricultural Scientists are Interested in Food Production

1) They study farm animals and crops in order to develop new ways of improving their quality and quantity (the amount produced).

2) Pests and weeds can seriously damage crops. Agricultural scientists investigate how to get rid of pests and weeds safely and effectively (removing them without damaging the crop itself).

3) Good soil is required to grow good crops. Agricultural scientists study how to maintain good quality soil.

4) Disease can damage crops. Some scientists are researching areas of biotechnology to provide solutions to problems like this. For example, agricultural scientists are looking at ways to alter the genetic material of plants and crops to make them more productive or resistant to disease.

5) Agricultural scientists also help to conserve water — they look after water supplies and research possible ways to save water.

Food Scientists are Employed in Lots of Areas

There are lots of areas of work in food science:

1) The food production and food processing industries.

2) Research — this includes looking for new food sources and substitutes for harmful additives (e.g. nitrites).

3) Sport — nutritionists and dieticians help athletes understand what they need to eat and drink to increase their performance.

4) Food analysts examine foods to determine how much fat, sugar, protein and vitamins they contain.

Food Production is Regulated

Food production is regulated for three important reasons:

1) Health and Safety — farms and factories involved in food production are checked regularly to make sure they're working in a safe manner and are looking after the health of the workers.

2) Animal welfare — by law animals must be treated humanely, including on the farm, during transportation, at market and at slaughter.

3) Environmental protection — it's important to make sure farming methods don't harm the environment, e.g. fertilisers can cause problems if they get into the water system.

The FSA and defra are two organisations that help to regulate food production:

The Food Standards Agency (FSA) — following an Act of Parliament in 2000, the FSA was set up by the Government. They are an independent agency, responsible for the entire UK food industry. They regulate the production, storage and transport of foods to protect consumer interests and public safety.

The Department for Environment, Food and Rural Affairs (Defra) is the Government department responsible for farming and food production. Defra looks after the interests of everyone involved in farming, agriculture and the environment. They aim to produce a sustainable, healthy and secure food supply.

Agricultural and food scientists — the heroes of the food production world

The work of scientists has greatly increased food production. Without these guys it would be slim pickings...

Food Poisoning

If you've ever had <u>food poisoning</u> you don't need me to tell you how gruesome it is. Urrghhh.
It's definitely best avoided, so read this page to make sure you know <u>what it is</u> and <u>what causes it</u>.

Food Poisoning *is Caused by* Microorganisms *in Food*

1) Food poisoning is usually caused by the presence of <u>microorganisms</u> (usually <u>bacteria</u>) in food.

2) These can make you ill if you ingest them, by <u>directly harming</u>
   your cells, or by <u>producing toxins</u> that poison you.

3) There are many different ones, but common problem bacteria are:

   <u>Campylobacter</u> — found in <u>dairy</u> and <u>poultry</u>.
   <u>Salmonella</u> — found in <u>poultry</u> and <u>eggs</u>.
   <u>E.coli</u> — usually found in <u>raw meat</u>.

4) Food poisoning can occur:
   • when food isn't <u>stored</u> or <u>cooked properly</u>,
   • through <u>poor kitchen or personal hygiene</u>,
   • through <u>contamination</u> from other sources.

The Symptoms *Depend on the* Type of Microorganism

The <u>type of microorganism</u> that you're infected with can affect:

1) The <u>symptoms</u> you get
   — these can include:
   • <u>stomach pains</u>
   • <u>vomiting</u>
   • <u>diarrhoea</u>

2) <u>How ill</u> you get, <u>how long</u> it lasts and <u>the time</u> it takes to
   start from when you've eaten the contaminated food.

Food Can Become Contaminated

In <u>mass food production</u> it's hard to prevent food from becoming contaminated.

1) Most of the contaminants are harmless, but some can cause <u>problems</u>
   e.g. plastic, glass, metal, banned additives, microorganisms and insects.

2) If food is <u>contaminated</u> people can get <u>ill</u> or <u>injured</u>. The manufacturer
   will have to <u>recall the product</u>, which can be <u>expensive</u> and <u>damaging</u> to the company's reputation.

3) Manufacturers must also tell you on the <u>label</u> exactly what's
   in (or <u>could</u> be in) the food, especially if any ingredients
   (e.g. peanuts or wheat) could trigger <u>allergies</u>.

AN EXPENSIVE FOOD RECALL Routine tests by Public Health Inspectors found that a sample of
Worcester sauce contained <u>Sudan 1</u>, a banned food colour. This was traced back to a batch of <u>chilli
powder</u> imported from India. A massive search took place to find all other products that had used
this Worcester sauce or chilli powder in their manufacture. The food companies involved had to
remove the contaminated products from shops and inform their customers and the Food Standards
Agency of the mistake. The incident cost them a fortune and may have damaged their reputation.

It was the salmon mousse I tell you...

Some <u>bacterial toxins</u> are really <u>poisonous</u> and can make you really <u>ill</u>, so watch out and don't eat <u>dodgy meat</u>.

Food Hygiene

Food poisoning is pretty unpleasant — and because I'm nice, I'll tell you how to avoid it.
All you need is good food hygiene. This is the careful care, preparation and storage of food.
Time to scrub up and get your hairnet on...

There are Five Main Ways to Keep Kitchens Hygienic

1 KEEP YOURSELF CLEAN

To make sure you're free of bacteria when handling food, you should:

1) Wash your hands — especially before preparing food, after handling raw meat, going to the toilet and after touching rubbish bins. It's not just fussiness — it's because microbes can stay alive on your hands for ages and can spread to everything that you touch.

2) Wear a hairnet or hat — just one hair can carry 100 000 microbes.

3) Cover all cuts and wounds to stop bacteria getting into the cuts and to stop any bacteria in the cuts getting into food.

4) Remove jewellery, e.g. rings, watches and bracelets — there could be millions of microbes underneath them. Urggh.

2 USE DISINFECTANTS AND DETERGENTS

1) Disinfectants (e.g. antibacterial cleaners and bleach) are chemicals that kill microbes. They're used for cleaning work surfaces and floors.

2) Detergents (e.g. washing-up liquid and washing powders) dissolve grease, oil and dirt. They deprive the microorganisms of the food they need to live.

3 USE HEAT TO STERILISE EQUIPMENT

Heat can be used to kill all the microbes on equipment, steam is often used to do this. In the home we use steam to sterilise things like babies' bottles.

In industry, equipment can also be sterilised using radiation e.g. gamma rays.

4 DISPOSE OF WASTE PROPERLY

Kitchen bins are like a giant breeding ground for microorganisms and they attract pests like rats and cockroaches to top it all off. So, they should be emptied regularly and should have a lid and a liner.

5 CONTROL PESTS

Animals aren't allowed anywhere near food preparation areas — they can carry harmful microorganisms. Here's how to deal with the common pests...

1) Mice and rats can be trapped or poisoned.

2) Cockroaches and other crawling insects can be trapped with glueboard traps (a sticky plastic sheet left out in areas where they are present).

3) Flying insects can be zapped with ultraviolet light traps — they're attracted to the light and fly into them, hitting an electric grid that kills them. You can stop them getting into the building in the first place by putting fine mesh screens over windows and chain curtains across doors.

Control pests — tie up your sister...

In industry these five things are really important to make sure food is safe to eat. In fact, they're actually a legal requirement. Hygiene standards are checked by Public Health Inspectors and if a place isn't up to scratch it risks being closed down. It's important to do these things at home as well though — so go and wash your hands.

Food Preservation

Food manufacturers <u>don't</u> want to give their customers <u>food poisoning</u> — that'd be pretty bad for business. The manufacturers <u>change the conditions</u> in the food to <u>reduce bacterial growth</u> (bacteria are a bit fussy about what conditions they'll grow in and if they're not right they won't grow — stubborn things).

Bacteria Like Warm, Moist Conditions

Bacteria can pretty much exist anywhere. The ones that make food go off and make you ill prefer:

- <u>Warmth</u> — this helps the <u>reactions</u> in bacteria to go faster, but only up to a certain point. They generally need temperatures from <u>5 to 62 °C</u>.
- <u>Moisture</u> — bacteria need <u>water</u> to survive.
- <u>Food source</u> — like all other organisms, they need food to grow. Greedy little blighters.
- Many bacteria also like a <u>neutral pH</u> (6.5 to 7.5).

The Growth of Bacteria Can be Slowed Down or Stopped

Depriving bacteria of the conditions they need to grow will either <u>slow</u> or <u>stop</u> their growth.

REFRIGERATION

Keeping food <u>below 5 °C</u> slows down the growth of any bacteria present in the food. It's just <u>too cold</u> for their reactions to work fast enough. Brrr.

Refrigeration doesn't stop the bacteria growing — it just slows it down.

FREEZING

In the freezing process, the <u>moisture</u> which bacteria need to thrive is <u>frozen</u>, so the bacteria can't grow and multiply. Freezers operate at around <u>–18 °C</u> (domestic) or <u>–32 °C</u> (industrial) — that's <u>far too cold</u> for most bacteria.

HEATING

Cooking food at the right temperature <u>kills bacteria</u> (as long as it's cooked right through). <u>Ultra-heat treatment</u> (UHT) is used in industry — foods like milk are heated to <u>132 °C for one minute</u> and then cooled really quickly to <u>destroy</u> any <u>microorganisms</u> and their <u>spores</u>.

Spores are reproductive cells produced by bacteria.

DRYING

<u>Drying</u> removes all the <u>moisture</u> (water) from a food. This <u>stops bacteria</u> being able to <u>digest</u> and <u>absorb</u> the food.

Osmosis is a fancy word used when water moves from areas with not much salt to areas with lots of salt.

SALTING

Adding salt means the bacteria <u>lose water from their cells by osmosis</u>. This <u>stops</u> them from <u>growing</u> and reproducing. Salt can be added to meat to make it last longer.

PICKLING

This involves storing food in <u>vinegar</u>, which has a <u>low pH</u> — it's <u>acidic</u>. Most bacteria prefer a neutral pH, so they <u>won't grow very fast</u> in the acidic conditions.

Mmmm... the nicest pickled onions you've ever seen.

If you don't learn this you'll be in a pickle...

Food manufacturers have to do this stuff to <u>stop</u> their food <u>going off</u> before it's on the shop shelves. It applies to home life too — some food needs refrigerating and you need to cook food properly.

Detecting Bacteria

Food products are regularly <u>tested</u> for bacteria by <u>microbiologists</u> (scientists that study microorganisms) and <u>Public Health Inspectors</u>. Food companies also conduct tests (to check the quality of their food).

Food Products <u>are</u> Tested for Bacteria...

1) <u>Public Health Inspectors</u> routinely test food from hotels, fast food outlets and supermarkets for bacteria to make sure <u>food is safe</u> and to <u>prevent outbreaks</u>.

2) If an outbreak of <u>food poisoning</u> does occur, food will be tested to find the <u>source</u>.

3) A sample of food is tested for:
   - The <u>amount</u> of bacteria in the food.
   - The presence of any <u>harmful bacteria</u>, e.g. *Salmonella*.

4) Certain <u>levels</u> of bacteria are <u>acceptable</u> — it's impossible to get rid of them all.

See the next page for how they do this.

...so are <u>Equipment</u> <u>and</u> <u>Surfaces</u>

1) In food production everything that food might come into <u>contact</u> with must be <u>clean</u>. This includes <u>equipment</u> as well as <u>work surfaces</u>.

2) <u>Regular checks</u> are carried out to ensure nothing harmful is lurking around which might <u>contaminate</u> the food during <u>preparation</u>.

3) Samples are taken from surfaces by <u>swabbing areas</u> using swabs (a bit like cotton buds). The swabs will then be taken to a lab to be <u>tested</u>.

<u>You Use</u> <u>Aseptic Techniques</u> <u>to</u> <u>Prevent Contamination</u> <u>of Samples</u>

<u>Aseptic techniques</u> are standard procedures used by microbiologists to <u>prevent contamination</u> — they should be used when <u>collecting</u> and <u>analysing</u> samples. This is done so you know that any bacteria you find <u>came from the food sample</u> (or surface or equipment) you were testing, not from a dirty lab bench or a grubby Petri dish etc. This is what you should do:

1) <u>Sterilise</u> all equipment <u>before</u> and <u>after</u> use.

2) Keep samples containing microorganisms in <u>sample bottles with lids</u>.

3) When opening a sample bottle to use it, <u>close it</u> again <u>as soon as possible</u>.

4) <u>Pass</u> the tops of sample bottles through a <u>Bunsen flame</u> whenever lids are <u>removed</u>.

5) <u>Don't</u> put lids down on <u>benches</u> — hold them with your <u>little finger</u> or your <u>other hand</u>.

6) Don't open Petri dishes <u>until</u> you are <u>ready to use them</u>.

7) Don't put any <u>equipment</u> that comes into <u>contact with microorganisms</u> down on <u>benches</u>.

8) <u>Seal</u> agar plates with sticky tape and <u>label</u> them with your <u>name</u>, the <u>date</u> and <u>what</u> you've put on the plate.

9) <u>Don't open</u> agar plates once they have been <u>sealed</u>.

10) <u>Dispose</u> of cultures <u>safely</u> — usually done by pressure sterilising in a machine called an <u>autoclave</u>.

An agar plate is a Petri dish containing a jelly-like substance called agar.

Don't forget you need to wear <u>gloves</u> and <u>protective clothing</u> when dealing with microbes. This stops microbes from you contaminating your sample and protects you from infection at the same time.

<u>There are more bacteria on the kitchen sink than in the toilet...</u>

All this aseptic technique stuff might seem like a lot to remember but it's all the same basic principle — be as <u>clean</u> and <u>safe</u> as possible, and don't leave things lying around with lids off. There are lots of bacteria in the air which could easily fall into your agar, so make sure you catch as few as possible.

Detecting Bacteria

The samples taken from surfaces, equipment or food are then analysed in a microbiology lab (by a microbiologist) to find out how many bacteria are present and what type they are. Sounds thrilling...

The Serial Dilution Method is Used to Count Bacteria

Serial dilutions are used to calculate how many bacteria are present in a sample — the original sample will contain too many bacteria for someone to count, so you dilute the sample again and again until there are few enough for you to count them. Here's how it's done:

1) You start by diluting your sample by mixing a little bit of it with water. Then it's diluted again and again etc.

2) A small amount of the final dilution is spread over an agar plate and incubated (placed in ideal conditions for growth). Each bacterial cell found in this final dilution will reproduce to produce a visible colony (a clump of bacteria).

3) The number of colonies is counted. If you know how many times the sample was diluted (and by how much, e.g. by a factor of 10), you can work out the approximate total number of cells in the original sample.

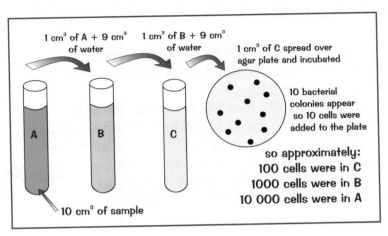

1 cm³ of A + 9 cm³ of water   1 cm³ of B + 9 cm³ of water   1 cm³ of C spread over agar plate and incubated

A   B   C

10 cm³ of sample

10 bacterial colonies appear so 10 cells were added to the plate

so approximately:
100 cells were in C
1000 cells were in B
10 000 cells were in A

You Make Streak Plates to Isolate Bacteria for Identification

If you take a swab from a surface or test food for bacteria it makes sense for you to find out what type of bacteria are present — so you know if there are any harmful ones present. Here's how you do it:

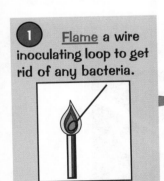

1 Flame a wire inoculating loop to get rid of any bacteria.

2 Dip the wire into the sample.

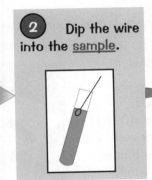

3 Using the wire loop spread the broth over an agar plate, so the bacteria are spread out as much as possible. Then incubate the agar plates (keep them warm) so the bacterial colonies grow.

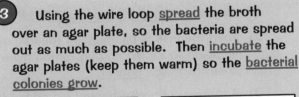

You need to use aseptic techniques when doing streak plates (and serial dilutions) because you need to know that the microorganisms that you've grown come from the sample (not from lab equipment or from the air).

4 A colony can be identified by removing it from the plate and staining the bacteria. Then you use a microscope to identify the type of bacteria.

Cereal dilutions — adding too much milk...

What the Public Health Inspectors do next depends on the results of these tests. If they find that a food sample contains way too many bacteria or a particularly harmful bacterium they might recall the product. If they find the same thing on surfaces or equipment they might shut down the restaurant, processing plant etc.

Microorganisms in Food

Not all microorganisms are bad. In fact, microorganisms such as bacteria, yeast and other fungi are really useful in food production. It sounds a bit yucky but there are plenty of foods that wouldn't taste nearly as nice without the help of bacteria and mould. Microbiologists study these microorganisms to work out exactly how we can use them to make useful products. They also investigate what factors affect the growth of microorganisms — this allows us to control conditions to get the best results in food production.

Bacteria are Used to Make Cheese...

Believe it or not, cheese doesn't come straight out of cows ready-packaged (that'd just be weird) — it's made by adding bacteria to milk like so:

1) A culture of bacteria is added to warm milk.
2) The bacteria convert lactose (the sugar in milk) to lactic acid.
3) This curdles the milk, producing solid curds.
4) The curds are separated from the liquid whey.
5) More bacteria are added to the curds, and the whole lot is left to ripen for a while.
6) Moulds are added to give blue cheese (e.g. Stilton) its colour and taste.

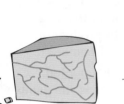

This woman is cutting up the solid curds so that she can drain off the liquid whey.

...and Yoghurt

Here's another surprise for you — tasty yoghurt is also made from milk using bacteria. Here's how:

1) All the equipment is sterilised to kill off any unwanted microorganisms.

2) Then the milk is pasteurised (heated up to 72 °C for 15 seconds) — again to kill off any unwanted microorganisms. Then the milk's cooled.

3) A starter culture of bacteria is added to the milk. The mixture is then incubated (heated to about 40 °C) in a vessel called a fermenter. The bacteria convert the lactose sugar in the milk into lactic acid — this is called fermentation. The lactic acid causes the milk to clot and solidify, turning it into yoghurt.

4) A sample is taken to make sure it's at the right consistency. Then flavours (e.g. fruit) and colours are sometimes added and the yoghurt is packaged.

Anyone for a nice pot of acidy milk, mmmmm...

The world's fastest yoghurt — pasteurised before you see it...

So there you have it — some microorganisms can help make really tasty food, like yoghurt. Yum. You still need to stop the bad microorganisms infecting your food though. That's why the milk is pasteurised — heating it kills off the unwanted microbes, making it perfectly safe and ready for your enjoyment.

Microorganisms in Food

Yeast is a type of fungus. It's pretty handy — it helps people make bread, beer and wine...

Yeast is Used to Make Bread

Holes in the bread, which make it nice and light, are made by carbon dioxide bubbles in the dough.

1) Yeast is used in dough to produce nice, light bread.
2) The yeast converts sugars to carbon dioxide and some ethanol.
3) This process is known as fermentation.
4) It's the carbon dioxide that makes the bread rise.
5) As the carbon dioxide expands, it gets trapped in the dough, making it lighter.

Brewing Beer and Wine Also Needs Yeast

There are five main steps to brewing beer and wine...

1 Firstly you need to get the sugar out of the barley or grapes:

BEER Beer is made from grain — usually barley. The grains are mashed up and soaked in water to produce a sugary solution with lots of bits in it. This is then sieved to remove the bits.

WINE Wine is made from grapes. These are mashed and water is added.

2 Yeast is added and the mixture is incubated (heated up):

BEER The yeast ferments maltose (the sugar in grain) into alcohol.

WINE The yeast ferments the sugars in the grape juice into alcohol.

3 The mixture is kept in fermenting vessels designed to stop unwanted microorganisms and air getting in.

The rising concentration of alcohol in the mixture eventually starts to kill the yeast. As the yeast dies, fermentation slows down.

4 The beer and wine produced is drawn off through a tap.

5 The drink is packaged ready for sale:

BEER The beer is usually then pasteurised — heated to kill any yeast left in the beer and completely stop fermentation. Finally the beer is casked ready for sale.

WINE Wine isn't pasteurised — any yeast left in the wine carries on slowly fermenting the sugar. This improves the taste of the wine. The wine is then bottled ready for sale.

You can't beat a loaf of freshly baked, carbon dioxide filled bread...

There are lots of fancy things you can do with beer which varies its taste — e.g. you can add hops to give a bitter flavour. The type of yeast used also affects the end product — e.g. lager uses a yeast which makes it all bubbly.

Revision Summary for Section 4

That section was a blast wasn't it... From food poisoning to detecting bacteria, all rounded off nicely with wine and cheese. Lovely. Give these questions a go to make sure you've got it all. If there's anything you're struggling with, just go back and have another read of the relevant pages. Then go and give your hands a good wash — you don't know where this book has been...

1) Name two areas where a food scientist might work.
2) Why is it important to regulate agriculture?
3) Name an organisation involved in the regulation of food production and describe its role.
4) Name three types of bacteria that cause food poisoning.
5) Give three symptoms of food poisoning.
6) Give two things that food can become contaminated with.
7) Explain why food contamination can be a problem.
8) What four things should you do to make sure you are clean before you start to prepare food?
9) What are disinfectants used for?
10) Why should you dispose of kitchen waste properly?
11) How could you control flies in a kitchen?
12) Describe the ideal conditions for the growth of harmful bacteria.
13) Describe six ways you can stop or slow down bacterial growth.
14) Why do health inspectors regularly test food products?
15) What two things are food samples tested for?
16) Why are food processing equipment and work surfaces tested for bacteria?
17) Why are aseptic techniques important when taking samples?
18)* A sample of milkshake is tested for bacteria. 1 cm³ of the sample is added to 9 cm³ of water. This dilution procedure is then repeated twice and 1 cm³ of the final dilution is spread on an agar plate and incubated. Six colonies grow. Approximately how many bacteria were present in the original 1 cm³ sample?
19) Describe how to make a streak plate to isolate a bacterium for identification.
20) Describe the process of making cheese.
21) Describe the process of making yoghurt.
22) In yoghurt making, why is the milk pasteurised?
23) Why is yeast used when making bread?
24) Describe the five main steps in brewing beer and wine.
25) When brewing wine or beer, what does yeast convert the sugar into?

*Answer on page 92.

Section 4 — Microorganisms and Food Production

Essential Nutrients

Agricultural scientists study how plants and animals grow and what we can do to help them grow bigger and better. They use the information from their research to help farmers to produce food.

Plants Need Minerals for Healthy Growth

1) Plants need certain chemical elements to help them grow.
2) They get these elements from minerals in the soil.
3) There are four main minerals that plants need:

1) Nitrates

Nitrates are needed for healthy leaf growth.

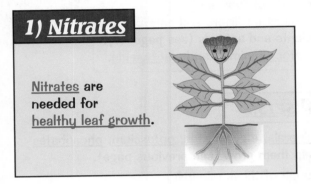

2) Phosphates

Phosphates are needed for good root development.

3) Potassium

Potassium is needed for a high fruit yield (lots of fruit).

4) Magnesium

Magnesium is needed for photosynthesis — see page 47).

The Minerals in Soil Need to be Replaced

1) Plants take essential nutrients from the soil in order to grow and reproduce.
2) When plants die they are broken down by microbes — so the nutrients are returned to the soil, ready for more plants to use.
3) But if the plants are taken away by the farmer (for us and other animals to eat) then the nutrients are also taken away.
4) This means the minerals in the soil aren't naturally replaced, and the farmer has to use other methods, like fertilisers, to replace them.
5) Farmers can use:

- Natural fertilisers — e.g. manure (animal waste) or compost.
- Chemical fertilisers — e.g. ammonium nitrate.

Nutrients are minerals that plants need to survive.

Compost is made of decomposed organic matter — leaves, waste food, etc.

Nitrates and phosphates and potassium, oh my...

When a farmer or a gardener buys fertiliser, they're pretty much buying a big bag of minerals to provide all the extra elements plants need to grow. The most important minerals to get into the soil are nitrates, which is why manure works well — it's full of nitrogenous waste excreted by animals. Lovely stuff. Smells pretty bad though.

Intensive Farming

Intensive farming is a method of farming developed by agricultural and food scientists. It's all about maximising the amount of food that can be produced, in the quickest and most cost effective way.

Scientists **Have Helped** Develop Intensive Farming Methods

Agricultural scientists study the growth of crops and farm animals. Their research has led to:

More Intensive Farming

Intensive farming is used to produce lots of food, quickly and cheaply. This includes using artificial fertilisers and carefully controlling growing conditions for plants and animals (see page 47). These practices greatly increase livestock (animal) and plant yields.

> The yield is how much food is produced in an area of land.

Intensive Farming **Uses** Artificial Fertilisers...

1) Plants need certain minerals, e.g. nitrates, potassium, phosphates and magnesium, to help them grow (see previous page).

2) If plants don't get enough of these minerals, their growth and health is affected.

3) Sometimes these minerals are missing from the soil because they've been used up by a previous crop.

4) Farmers use artificial fertilisers to replace these missing minerals or provide more of them.

5) This helps to increase the crop yield.

...As Well As Pesticides, Fungicides **and** Herbicides

1) PESTICIDES are chemicals that kill farm pests, e.g. insects, rats and mice. Pesticides that kill insects are called insecticides. Killing pests that would otherwise eat the crop means there's more left for us.

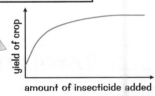

[graph: y-axis labelled "yield of crop", x-axis labelled "amount of insecticide added", curve rising and levelling off]

2) FUNGICIDES kill fungi, e.g. moulds that can damage crops.

3) HERBICIDES kill weeds. If you remove plants that compete for the same resources (e.g. nutrients from the soil), it means the crop gets more of them and so grows better.

Advances in Technology **Have Made Intensive Farming** Easier

Intensive farming has been made more efficient by advances in technology:

1) Advances in science and technology mean that new methods of growing crops and rearing animals can be used to help farmers produce crops and livestock more cheaply and quickly.

2) After crops have been harvested, they need to be kept as fresh as possible for as long as possible. If they don't get to the shops in a good condition people won't buy them and the farmers lose money.

3) Improved storage, refrigeration and transportation of food has helped to make this easier for farmers.

Intensive farming might just crop up in the exam...

The research done by agricultural scientists allows farmers to produce lots of food, quickly and cheaply. The farmers make more money and food is cheaper for us to buy in the shops. Happy farmers, happy shoppers.

More on Intensive Farming

Farmers who use intensive farming <u>carefully control</u> the <u>environment</u> that plants and animals are kept in.
They use as <u>little space</u> and as <u>few resources</u> as possible, to make the <u>largest quantity</u> of produce they can.

<u>Animals</u> can be Kept in <u>Controlled Environments</u>

1) Animals use energy from <u>respiration</u> to <u>keep warm</u> and <u>move around</u>.

2) <u>Using up energy</u> means that the animals <u>lose weight</u>.

See page 11 for more on respiration.

3) In countries like the UK, animals such as <u>pigs</u> and <u>chickens</u>
are often <u>intensively farmed</u> (battery farming).

4) This means that they're kept <u>close together indoors</u> in
small pens, so that they're <u>warm</u> and <u>can't move about</u>.

5) This saves them <u>wasting energy</u> on movement, and
stops them giving out as much energy as <u>heat</u>.

6) This <u>reduces</u> the amount of <u>body weight</u> they lose.

7) So, as long as the animals have a <u>good food supply</u>,
they will grow <u>faster</u> on <u>less food</u>.

8) Farmers also need to <u>control</u> the <u>light</u> and <u>ventilation</u> reaching the animals.
Good ventilation and plenty of light helps to keep the animals <u>healthy</u>.

9) Keeping animals in <u>controlled conditions</u> makes things <u>cheaper</u> for the
farmer, and for us when the animals finally turn up on supermarket shelves.

<u>Plants</u> can be Kept in <u>Controlled Environments</u> <u>Too</u>

1) Plants make their own <u>food</u> by <u>photosynthesis</u>:

$$\text{Carbon dioxide} + \text{Water} \xrightarrow{\text{LIGHT ENERGY}} \text{Glucose} + \text{Oxygen}$$

2) They use the glucose they produce to <u>grow</u>.

3) Farmers can help <u>increase plant growth</u> by providing the
<u>best conditions</u> for <u>photosynthesis</u> in greenhouses.

4) <u>Light</u> is always needed for photosynthesis, so farmers often
<u>supply artificial light</u> after the Sun goes down to give their
plants more quality photosynthesis time.

5) Carbon dioxide is also needed for photosynthesis, so farmers
<u>increase</u> the level of <u>carbon dioxide</u> in their greenhouses.
They can do this by burning fuel which makes carbon dioxide
as a by-product.

6) Farmers need to carefully <u>control</u> the <u>ventilation</u> in the
greenhouse. This is to reduce the <u>humidity</u> (moisture) inside the
greenhouse and to make sure that the plants don't get <u>too hot</u>.

7) Greenhouses also <u>trap</u> the <u>Sun's heat</u> so that it doesn't get too
cold for the plants.

<u>Intensive farming — the agricultural version of fast food...</u>

now you know all about <u>intensive farming</u>. The important bit is knowing <u>how</u> it <u>increases</u> the amount of
od produced. <u>Controlling</u> the <u>conditions</u> that <u>animals</u> are kept in allows farmers to <u>fatten them up</u> cheaply and
ickly. Providing the best conditions for <u>photosynthesis</u> in plants just helps nature along — ahhh, isn't it lovely.

Organic Farming

Intensive farming methods are <u>still used</u> a lot. But people are also using <u>organic</u> methods more and more.

Organic Farming Doesn't Use Artificial Chemicals

An alternative to modern intensive farming is <u>organic farming</u>. Organic methods are more <u>traditional</u>. Where intensive farming uses artificial fertilisers, herbicides, pesticides and fungicides, organic farming has more <u>natural alternatives</u>.

THE LAND IS KEPT FERTILE BY:

1) <u>Using organic fertilisers</u> (i.e. animal manure and compost). This <u>recycles</u> the nutrients left in plant and animal waste. It <u>doesn't always work as well</u> as artificial fertilisers, but it's better for the <u>environment</u>.

2) <u>Crop rotation</u> — growing a cycle of <u>different crops</u> in a field each year. This stops the <u>pests</u> and <u>diseases</u> of one crop building up, and means <u>nutrients</u> are less likely to run out (as each crop has <u>different needs</u>).

PESTS AND WEEDS ARE CONTROLLED BY:

1) <u>Weeding</u> — <u>physically removing</u> the weeds, rather than just spraying them with a <u>herbicide</u>. Obviously it takes a lot longer, but there are no nasty <u>chemicals</u> involved.

2) <u>Varying crop growing times</u> — farmers can <u>avoid</u> the <u>major pests</u> for a certain crop by <u>planting</u> it <u>later</u> or <u>earlier</u> in the season. This means they <u>won't need pesticides</u>.

3) <u>Using natural pesticides</u> — some pesticides are completely natural, and so long as they're used <u>responsibly</u> they don't mess up the ecosystem.

4) <u>Biological control</u> — biological control means using a <u>predator</u>, a <u>parasite</u> or a <u>disease</u> to kill the pest, instead of chemicals. For example:

   a) <u>Aphids</u> are pests which eat roses and vegetables. <u>Ladybirds</u> are aphid <u>predators</u>, so people release them into their fields and gardens to keep aphid numbers down.

   b) Certain types of <u>wasps</u> and <u>flies</u> produce larvae which develop on (or in, yuck) a host insect. This eventually kills the host. Lots of insect pests have <u>parasites</u> like this.

Organic Farms Keep Animals in More Natural Conditions

1) For an animal farm to be classified as "organic", it has to follow <u>guidelines</u> on the <u>ethical treatment</u> of animals.

2) This means <u>no</u> battery farming — animals have to be free to roam outdoors for a certain number of hours every day.

3) Animals also have to be fed on <u>organically-grown feed</u> that doesn't contain any artificial chemicals.

Don't get bugged by biological pest control...

The <u>Soil Association</u> is an organisation that certifies farms and products as <u>organic</u>. They have very strict rules about what products can carry their logo — much stricter than the European Union and UK Government's minimum standards. About <u>80%</u> of all organic food sold in the UK is Soil Association approved. Fancy that.

Comparing Farming Methods

It's all very well knowing how the different farming methods work, but are they actually any good? Both intensive and organic methods have advantages and disadvantages, which I'm afraid you just have to learn.

Intensive Farming is Efficient but can Damage the Environment

The main advantages of intensive farming methods are that they produce large amounts of food in a very small space, and it's cheaper for us. But they can cause a few problems — the main effects are:

1) Removal of hedges to make huge great fields for maximum efficiency.
   This destroys the natural habitat of wild creatures and can lead to serious soil erosion.
2) Lots of people think that intensive farming of animals such as battery hens is cruel.
3) The crowded conditions in factory farms create a favourable environment for the spread of disease.
4) If too much fertiliser is applied, it can find its way into rivers and lakes, causing the death of many fish.
5) Pesticides can build up to toxic levels in animals like otters and birds of prey.

Organic Farming Has Advantages and Disadvantages Too

ADVANTAGES

1) Organic farming uses fewer chemicals, so there's less risk of toxic chemicals remaining on food.
2) It's better for the environment. There's less chance of polluting rivers with fertiliser.
   Organic farmers also avoid using pesticides, so don't disrupt food chains and harm wildlife.
3) Organic farms allow animals to live in natural conditions so that they have a better quality of life.
4) Many people feel that the quality of organic food is better, e.g. the flavour.

DISADVANTAGES

1) Organic farming takes up more space than intensive farming — so more land has to be farmland, rather than being set aside for wildlife or for other uses.
2) It's more labour-intensive and takes more time. This provides more jobs, but it also makes the food more expensive.
3) You can't grow as much food as you can with intensive farming.

Some people will pay more for an organic product if they know it's been produced in a more environmentally friendly way.

You Can Investigate the Best Conditions for Plant Growth

To investigate how well plants grow, stick some seeds (e.g. radish seeds) in some pots, vary the conditions and see which ones grow the best. Sounds easy — but here are some things you've got to consider:

1) Which **VARIABLE** are you investigating?
   This could be temperature, amount of water or light, type of fertiliser, overcrowding, or presence of a herbicide. You have to make sure that every other variable remains the same throughout the experiment — this is usually the hard bit.

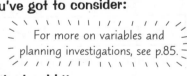

For more on variables and planning investigations, see p.85.

For more on variables and planning investigations, see p.85.

2) How are you going to **MEASURE** the growth?
   You could count the number of leaves, or measure the plant's height or mass.
   (Or, if you're anything like me, which one stays alive the longest.)

You should repeat the experiment a couple of times, to make sure you get the same results — this makes your results more reliable.

There's nowt wrong wi' spreadin' muck on it...

You may well have quite a strong opinion on stuff like intensive farming of animals — whether it's 'tree-hugging hippie liberals, just give me a bit of nice cheap pork,' or 'poor creatures, they should be free, free as the wind!' Either way, keep it to yourself and give a nice, balanced argument in the exam.

Selective Breeding and Genetic Engineering

Selective breeding has been developed so that farmers can grow plants and animals with the best characteristics. As I'm sure most farmers will agree, it's a handy little trick to know...

Selective Breeding is Very Useful in Farming

Farmers can select plants or animals to breed so that their offspring will develop certain characteristics. This is called selective breeding. Here's how it's done:

1) From the existing stock, the organisms that have the best characteristics are selected.

2) They're bred with each other.

3) The best of the offspring are selected and bred.

4) This process is repeated over several generations to develop the desired traits.

5) By selecting certain plants or animals, scientists can...

- Choose the best characteristics — e.g. to get higher milk yields, tastier meat, bigger eggs, etc.
- Increase tolerance — so crops or animals are able to thrive in a larger range of climates.
- Grow a uniform crop — i.e. plants of the same size, or a crop that is ready to harvest at the same time.

6) The main drawback is a reduced gene pool. This is where the variation in a population is reduced because the farmer keeps breeding from the "best" animals or plants.

7) This can be a serious problem if a new disease appears. All the stock are very similar to each other, so if one of them is going to be killed by a new disease, the others are likely to die from it too. Bad news.

Genes are Transferred in Genetic Engineering

Scientists have now come up with a more efficient way of producing organisms with all the desired characteristics — genetic engineering.

1) Genetic engineering is where genes are transferred from one organism to another.

2) 'Foreign' genes (ones from another organism) can be transferred into plant or animal cells at an early stage in their development.

3) The characteristics that develop depend on the gene inserted. The possibilities are endless. For example, long-life tomatoes can be made by changing the gene that causes fruit to ripen.

> A gene is a short bit of DNA that controls one of an organism's characteristics.

Genetic Engineering Has Advantages and Risks

Genetic engineering could completely change how we produce food — but there are also potential dangers.

1) The main advantage is that you can produce organisms with new and very useful features.

2) The world's population is increasing — we need to produce enough food to feed everyone. Genetically modified crops could be the answer, as they have a greater yield and can grow in more hostile places.

3) But it's big business, and farmers may suffer if they can't compete with big biotechnology companies.

4) The main risk is that the inserted gene could have unexpected harmful effects. E.g. genes inserted into bacteria could mutate and the bacteria could become pathogenic (disease causing). People also worry about the engineered DNA 'escaping' — e.g. crops can be engineered to be herbicide resistant but if these genes passed into a weed then they'd be unstoppable.

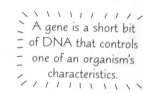

Selective breeding — sounds like a night out at my local disco...

Selective breeding and genetic engineering have exciting possibilities, but they should be treated with caution...

Higher

Making Chemicals for Farming

Scientists use <u>chemical reactions</u> to produce all the <u>fancy chemicals</u> farmers need to produce food.

Chemicals for Farming **Need to be** Economical **to** Produce

1) Producing <u>chemicals for farming</u> is a <u>big industry</u>.

2) <u>Fertilisers</u>, <u>pesticides</u>, <u>insecticides</u> and <u>herbicides</u> are all made using <u>chemical reactions</u>.

3) These reactions needs to be <u>carefully controlled</u> to make sure the chemicals are produced <u>cheaply</u>.

4) Producers of these chemicals need to:

- Consider the <u>price</u> of the <u>equipment</u> and <u>materials</u>.
- Consider the <u>cost</u> of the <u>energy required</u> to make the chemical reactions occur.
- Make sure as little <u>waste</u> as possible is produced.

Neutralisation Reactions **are Used to Make** Artificial Fertilisers

1) <u>Nitrogen</u> is really <u>important</u> for <u>plant growth</u> — it's found in <u>nitrates</u> (see page 45).

2) <u>Artificial fertilisers</u> contain <u>soluble chemical compounds</u>, that provide <u>nitrogen</u> to the plants.

3) They <u>replace</u> missing nitrogen from the soil, or provide <u>more</u> nitrogen.

Soluble means that they can dissolve.

4) This helps to increase <u>crop yield</u>, as the crops can grow <u>faster</u> and <u>bigger</u>.

5) <u>Ammonium nitrate</u> is a common nitrogen-containing fertiliser. It is made using a <u>neutralisation reaction</u>:

> **Ammonia + Nitric acid → Ammonium nitrate + Water**
> (base)   (acid)   (fertiliser)

A neutralisation reaction is when an acid and a base react to form a salt.

Percentage **Yield Compares** Actual **and** Theoretical **Yield**

Agricultural scientists use <u>yields</u> to make sure that <u>chemical reactions</u> are <u>efficient</u>.

1) The <u>actual yield</u> of a chemical reaction is the <u>mass of the products</u>.

2) The <u>theoretical yield</u> is the mass of products you <u>expect</u> to get.

3) The <u>percentage yield</u> compares the actual yield with the theoretical yield
— it tells you <u>how successful</u> the chemical reaction was.

4) Percentage yield is given by the <u>formula</u>:

$$\text{percentage yield} = \frac{\text{actual yield (grams)}}{\text{theoretical yield (grams)}} \times 100$$

EXAMPLE

Robert is <u>making a fertiliser</u> using nitric acid and ammonia. The <u>theoretical yield</u> of ammonium nitrate is <u>1500 g</u>. His <u>actual yield</u> is <u>900 g</u>. Calculate the <u>percentage yield</u> of Robert's reaction.

$$\text{percentage yield} = \frac{900 \text{ g}}{1500 \text{ g}} \times 100$$
$$= 0.6 \times 100 = \underline{\textbf{60\%}}$$

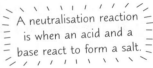

5) Percentage yield is <u>always</u> somewhere between 0 and 100%.

6) A <u>100%</u> yield means that you got <u>all</u> the product you expected to get.

7) A <u>0%</u> yield means that <u>no</u> reactants were converted into product, i.e. <u>no product</u> at all was made.

In reality, you'll never get a 100% yield. This could be for loads of different reasons, e.g. incomplete reactions, loss of product when transferring between containers, etc.

Get that percentage yield nice and high...

..making fertilisers is all about <u>making money</u>. <u>Higher yields = more money</u>. Ka-ching.

Controlling Chemical Reactions

The speed of a chemical reaction depends on <u>four</u> things — <u>temperature</u>, <u>concentration</u> (or <u>pressure</u> for gases) whether a <u>catalyst</u> is used and the <u>size of the particles</u>. This page explains <u>why</u> these affect the reaction speed

More Collisions Increases the Speed of the Reaction

Reactions happen if <u>particles collide</u>. The <u>more often</u> and <u>harder</u> they collide, the <u>quicker</u> the reaction occurs

1) Increasing the Temperature Increases the Speed of the Reaction

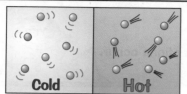
Cold   Hot

1) When the <u>temperature is increased</u> the particles all <u>move quicker</u>.
2) If they're moving quicker, they're going to <u>collide more often</u>.
3) Higher temperatures also means <u>the collisions</u> are more <u>energetic</u>.
4) So the <u>speed</u> of the chemical reaction <u>increases</u>.

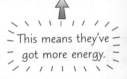

~ This means they've ~
~ got more energy. ~

2) Increasing the Concentration or Pressure Increases the Speed of the Reaction

1) If a solution is made more <u>concentrated</u> it means there are more particles of <u>reactant</u> in the same volume, so they'll <u>collide more often</u>.

2) In a <u>gas</u>, increasing the <u>pressure</u> means the molecules are <u>more crowded</u>, so there are more collisions.

3) This means the <u>speed</u> of the chemical reaction <u>increases</u>.

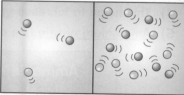

Low Concentration   High Concentration
(Low Pressure)   (High Pressure)

3) Using Smaller Particles Increases the Speed of the Reaction

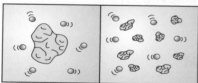

big lump =   smaller pieces =
small surface area   large surface area

1) If one of the reactants is a <u>solid lump</u> then <u>breaking it up</u> into <u>smaller</u> pieces (like a <u>powder</u>) will <u>increase its surface area</u>.

2) This means the particles of the other reactant will have <u>more area</u> to work on so they'll <u>collide more often</u>.

3) <u>More frequent collisions</u> means the <u>speed</u> of the chemical reaction <u>increases</u>.

4) A Catalyst Increases the Speed of the Reaction

1) A <u>catalyst</u> is a substance which increases the <u>speed of a reaction</u>, <u>without</u> being chemically <u>changed</u> or <u>used up</u> in the reaction.

2) Because it isn't used up, you only need a <u>tiny bit</u> of it to catalyse <u>large amounts</u> of reactants.

3) Catalysts tend to be very <u>fussy</u> about which reactions they catalyse though — you can't just stick any old catalyst in a reaction and expect it to work.

Collision theory — it's always the other driver...

It may sound a bit weird but all this stuff is pretty much just common sense. You just have to remember that <u>particles colliding more often</u> = a <u>faster reaction</u>. It's a bit like the dodgems really... If you go really fast or put more people in dodgem cars or create loads more mini-sized dodgems you'll crash more. Excellent.

Reversible Reactions and Ammonia Production

This page is all about <u>reversible reactions</u>. Sound good? Then read on...

> **A <u>REVERSIBLE REACTION</u> is one where the <u>PRODUCTS</u> of the reaction can <u>THEMSELVES REACT</u> to produce the <u>ORIGINAL REACTANTS</u>**
>
> $$A + B \rightleftharpoons C + D$$

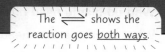

The '$\rightleftharpoons$' shows the reaction goes <u>both ways</u>.

Reversible Reactions <u>Will Reach</u> <u>Equilibrium</u>

1) As the <u>reactants</u> (A and B) react via the <u>forward reaction</u>, the <u>products</u> (C and D) will be created.

2) Once C and D <u>exist</u>, they can react via the <u>backwards reaction</u> to produce more A and B.

3) After a while the forward reaction will be going at <u>exactly the same speed</u> as the backward one — this is <u>equilibrium</u>.

4) At equilibrium <u>both</u> reactions are still <u>happening</u>, but there's <u>no overall effect</u> — the <u>concentrations</u> of reactants and products <u>won't change</u>.

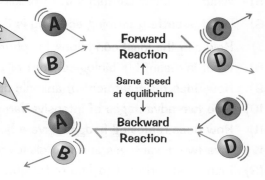

Forward Reaction

↑ Same speed at equilibrium ↓

Backward Reaction

The <u>Position of Equilibrium</u> <u>Can be on the</u> <u>Right</u> <u>or the</u> <u>Left</u>

When a reaction's at equilibrium it <u>doesn't</u> mean the amounts of reactants and products are <u>equal</u>.

1) Sometimes the equilibrium will <u>lie to the right</u> — "<u>lots of the products and not much of the reactants</u>".

2) Sometimes the equilibrium will <u>lie to the left</u> — "<u>lots of the reactants but not much of the products</u>".

<u>Nitrogen</u> <u>and</u> <u>Hydrogen</u> <u>Are Needed to Make</u> <u>Ammonia</u>

1) <u>Ammonia</u> (NH_3), is used to make <u>ammonium nitrate</u>. This is a key ingredient in <u>fertilisers</u> (see page 46).

2) Ammonia is produced using a <u>reversible reaction</u>:

$$N_{2\,(g)} + 3H_{2\,(g)} \rightleftharpoons 2NH_{3\,(g)}$$

3) <u>Nitrogen</u> and <u>hydrogen</u> react to form <u>ammonia</u>. Because the reaction is <u>reversible</u>, the ammonia can break down again into nitrogen and hydrogen. After a while the reaction will reach <u>equilibrium</u>.

4) The <u>position</u> of <u>equilibrium</u>, and therefore the <u>yield</u> of <u>ammonia</u>, is affected by <u>temperature</u> and <u>pressure</u>.

5) <u>Higher pressures</u> favour the <u>forward reaction</u>, so a high pressure is used to give the best percentage yield.

6) However, <u>high temperatures</u> will actually move the equilibrium the <u>wrong way</u> — away from ammonia and towards N_2 and H_2.

7) This means that the <u>yield</u> of ammonia would be <u>greater</u> at <u>lower temperatures</u>.

8) The problem with this is that lower temperatures means a <u>slower reaction speed</u>.

9) So what they do is <u>increase</u> the <u>temperature</u> anyway, to get a much <u>faster reaction speed</u>.

10) This is a <u>compromise</u> between <u>maximum yield</u> and <u>speed of reaction</u> — it's better to wait just 20 seconds for a 10% yield than to have to wait 60 seconds for a 20% yield.

quilibrium — lots of activity without much happening...*

ver the page and scribble down as much as you can remember, then check, and try again.

bit like the England football team really.

Revision Summary for Section 5

Hmm... so this whole farming lark, what's that all about? Well, if you don't know, you haven't read this section properly, and your first task is to go back and read it all again. However, if you think you know your intensive farming methods from your organic farming methods, here are some questions for you.

1)   Why do plants need nitrates?
2)   What is magnesium needed for?
3)   Why do farmers need to add minerals to the soil?
4)   Why does intensive farming use fertilisers?
5)   What is a chemical that's used to kill weeds called?
6)   What is battery farming and why is it used?
7)   How can the ideal conditions for photosynthesis be artificially created in greenhouses?
8)   What is meant by 'biological control'?
9)   How does the treatment of animals differ between organic and intensive farming?
10) Give two advantages of intensive farming.
11) How does removing hedges have a bad effect on the environment?
12) Give two advantages and two disadvantages of organic farming.
13) Plan an experiment to find out if you get better plant growth using compost or soil from a garden. Give three variables you'll need to keep constant. How would you measure the growth?
14) Why do people selectively breed livestock?
15) What is the main drawback of selective breeding?
16) What is the main advantage of genetic engineering?
17) Give one potential risk of using genetic engineering.
18) a) What is the formula for percentage yield?
     b) How does percentage yield differ from actual yield?
19)*The theoretical yield of a reaction is 3000 g. The actual yield is 2400 g. Calculate the percentage yield of the reaction.
20) True or False: The more often particles collide, the slower the speed of a chemical reaction.
21) What four things affect the speed of a reaction?
22) What is a reversible reaction? Explain why it could reach an equilibrium.
23) a) Write out the equation for the reversible reaction that produces ammonia.
     b) What effect does increasing the pressure have on this reaction?
     c) What effect does increasing the temperature have on this reaction?

*Answer on page 92.

Roles of Analytical Scientists

This page is all about the people who analyse scientific evidence. Analytical scientists are found in forensic services, manufacturing and pharmaceutical industries, healthcare and public protection. They answer questions and solve problems...

Forensic Scientists Help with Criminal Investigations

Forensic scientists examine substances found at crime scenes that might be useful for solving crimes — they work in laboratories and may have to appear as witnesses in court.

Some of the things that forensic scientists are responsible for include:

1) Identifying and analysing blood and other bodily fluids.
2) Identifying and comparing fibres, plant and animal materials.
3) Examining and comparing chips of paint and glass fragments.
4) Analysing and comparing fingerprints.

Environmental Scientists Protect the Environment

Environmental scientists collect and analyse evidence about the environment, and do work that protects and improves our environment. They work outdoors, in laboratories and in offices.

Some of the things that environmental scientists are responsible for include:

1) Monitoring and improving air and water quality.
2) Investigating and monitoring pollution.
3) Monitoring and testing industrial waste to make sure businesses aren't breaking environmental protection laws.
4) Working with industries and businesses to reduce waste and pollution, and increase recycling.

> Lots of environmental scientists work for Defra (the Department for Environment, Food and Rural Affairs).

Pharmaceutical Scientists Help Develop New Drugs

Pharmaceutical scientists test new drugs and suggest improvements. They work in laboratories and factories.

Some of the things that pharmaceutical scientists are responsible for include:

1) Analysing drugs to make sure they are stable, effective and don't have any harmful side effects.
2) Monitoring the quality of drugs produced during manufacturing.
3) Working out how and why drugs work so that they can be improved.

Healthcare Scientists Help Diagnose Diseases

Healthcare scientists analyse samples to help doctors diagnose what's wrong with a patient. They work in hospital laboratories, doctors' clinics and for public health laboratories.

Some of the things that healthcare scientists are responsible for include:

1) Analysing fluid samples (e.g. blood or urine samples) to help identify diseases.
2) Examining tissue samples to look for clues that could help to diagnose a patient.

Who you gonna call? Yep, those crazy analytical scientists — that's who...

So, if you're a dab hand at science and problem solving, a career as an analytical scientist could be for you.

Ionic Compounds

Analytical scientists often have to perform chemical tests to find out what substances are present in a sampl
That's what the rest of this section is all about — chemical analysis.

You can Identify Substances by Looking at Their Characteristics

1) Different substances have different characteristics. For example:

   - Different substances have different melting and boiling points.
   - Some substances dissolve in water while others don't.

2) You can use these characteristics to identify substances.

3) The characteristics of a substance depend on its structure and bonding.

Ionic Compounds Have a Giant Lattice Structure

Many solids you'll encounter in your day-to-day life are ionic.

1) Ionic compounds are made of charged particles called ions.

2) Metal ions are always positively charged.

3) Non-metal ions are usually negatively charged.

4) Ions with opposite charges are strongly attracted to one another.

5) This gives ionic compounds a close, regular structure called a giant lattice. They look a bit like this.

A common example is sodium chloride (table salt). It has positive sodium ions (the metal ions) and negative chloride ions (the non-metal ions).

Ionic Compounds Have High Melting Points

strong forces of attraction

1) The forces of attraction between the ions are very strong.

2) This makes it difficult to separate the ions — it takes a lot of energy to overcome the forces.

3) To melt ionic compounds you have to separate the ions.

4) So ionic compounds have high melting points.

5) Which makes them solids at room temperature.

The force that holds ions together is called electrostatic attraction.

Some Ionic Compounds Dissolve in Water

Some ionic compounds are soluble in water, but some aren't. This makes life a little more difficult for you, but a little easier for analytical scientists when they're trying to work out which ionic compound they have. Here are some really handy rules:

1) All sodium (Na^+), potassium (K^+) and ammonium (NH_4^+) salts are SOLUBLE in water.

2) All nitrates (NO_3^-) are SOLUBLE in water.

3) Most chlorides (Cl^-) are SOLUBLE in water, except for silver and lead.

4) Most sulfates are SOLUBLE in water, except for barium and lead. Calcium sulfate is slightly soluble.

5) Most oxides (O^{2-}), hydroxides (OH^-) and carbonates (CO_3^{2-}) are INSOLUBLE in water, except for sodium and potassium.

Giant ionic lattices — all over your chips...

To identify the metal ion in an ionic compound, you could use the flame test on p.59 or the precipitation test with sodium hydroxide on p.61. The non-metal ion could be a carbonate (p.60), sulfate (p.61) or chloride (p.61). You can even test the compound's solubility using the method on p.60. All this yet to come... lucky you.

Formulas of Ionic Compounds

Once the <u>positive</u> and <u>negative</u> ions in an <u>ionic compound</u> have been identified you can work out the <u>formula</u>.

The <u>Charges</u> in an <u>Ionic Compound</u> Add Up to Zero

Different ions have <u>different charges</u>, shown in the table: ➡️

Some metals (like iron, copper and tin) can form ions with <u>different charges</u>. The number <u>in brackets</u> after the name tells you the <u>size</u> of the <u>positive charge</u> on the ion — and luckily for us, this makes the charge really easy to remember.

E.g. an iron(II) ion has a charge of $2+$, so it's Fe^{2+}.

The main thing to remember is that in compounds the <u>total charge must always add up to zero</u>.

Positive Ions		Negative Ions	
Lithium	Li^+	Chloride	Cl^-
Sodium	Na^+	Cyanide	CN^-
Potassium	K^+	Oxide	O^{2-}
Magnesium	Mg^{2+}	Carbonate	CO_3^{2-}
Calcium	Ca^{2+}	Sulfate	SO_4^{2-}
Iron(II)	Fe^{2+}	Hydroxide	OH^-
Iron(III)	Fe^{3+}	Nitrate	NO_3^-
Aluminium	Al^{3+}		

The <u>Easy</u> Ones

If the ions in the compound have the <u>same size charge</u> then it's easy.

> **EXAMPLE: Find the formula for <u>calcium oxide</u>.**
>
> Find the charges on a calcium ion and an oxide ion.
>
> A calcium ion is Ca^{2+} and an oxide ion is O^{2-}.
>
> To balance the total charge you need one calcium ion to every one oxide ion.
> So the formula of calcium oxide must be: **CaO**

> **EXAMPLE: Find the formula for <u>potassium cyanide</u>.**
>
> Find the charges on a potassium ion and a cyanide ion.
>
> A potassium ion is K^+ and a cyanide ion is CN^-.
>
> To balance the total charge you need one potassium ion to every one cyanide ion.
> So the formula of potassium cyanide must be: **KCN**

The <u>Slightly Harder</u> Ones

If the ions have different size charges, you need to put in some numbers to balance things up.

> **EXAMPLE: Find the formula for <u>sodium oxide</u>.**
>
> Find the charges on a sodium ion and an oxide ion.
>
> A sodium ion is Na^+ and an oxide ion is O^{2-}.
>
> To balance the total charge you need two sodium ions to every one oxide ion.
> So the formula of sodium oxide must be: **Na_2O**

> **EXAMPLE: Find the formula for <u>aluminium chloride</u>.**
>
> Find the charges on an aluminium ion and a chloride ion.
>
> An aluminium ion is Al^{3+} and a chloride ion is Cl^-.
>
> To balance the total charge you need one aluminium ion to every three chloride ions.
> So the formula of aluminium chloride must be: **$AlCl_3$**

The <u>Dead Hard</u> Ones

You'll need to do a fair bit of balancing to get these ones sorted.

> **EXAMPLE: Find the formula for <u>aluminium oxide</u>.**
>
> Find the charges on an aluminium ion and an oxide ion.
>
> An aluminium ion is Al^{3+} and an oxide ion is O^{2-}.
>
> Two Al^{3+} ions carry a total charge of $6+$. Three O^{2-} ions carry a total charge of $6-$. $6+$ balances out $6-$.
> So the formula of aluminium oxide must be: **Al_2O_3**

> **EXAMPLE: Find the formula for <u>iron(III) sulfate</u>.**
>
> Find the charges on an iron(III) ion and a sulfate ion.
>
> An iron(III) ion is Fe^{3+} and a sulfate ion is SO_4^{2-}.
>
> Two Fe^{3+} ions carry a total charge of $6+$. Three SO_4^{2-} ions carry a total charge of $6-$. $6+$ balances out $6-$.
> So the formula of iron(III) sulfate must be: **$Fe_2(SO_4)_3$**

Any old ion, any old ion — any, any, any old ion...

After all those examples, I'm sure you could work out the formula of <u>any ionic compound</u>. And just to test that theory here are a few for you to try: a) magnesium oxide,   b) lithium oxide,   c) sodium sulfate.*

Covalent Compounds

Analytical scientists could also come across covalent compounds. These substances may well come from living materials. So they could be dealing with blood, guts and gore. Ughh!

Many Covalent Substances Come from Living Materials

Many substances obtained from living materials are organic compounds.

1) Organic compounds tend to have covalent bonding (see below).

2) Covalent substances usually contain non-metals.

Analytical scientists analyse covalent compounds in fluids, like blood and urine, to help identify the substances present in a sample.

Organic covalent compounds, e.g. ethanol, glucose, drugs

1) Ethanol (C_2H_5OH) — The concentration of ethanol (alcohol) in the blood is measured to find out if someone's 'over the limit' whilst driving (see page 62).

2) Glucose ($C_6H_{12}O_6$) — The concentration of glucose in the blood and in urine can indicate if a person is diabetic.

3) Drugs — Blood analysis can show if a person's taken illegal drugs, e.g. ecstasy or cocaine.

Inorganic covalent compounds, e.g. water, carbon dioxide

1) Water (H_2O) — If water's found in the lungs of a body it suggests that they've died from drowning.

2) Carbon dioxide (CO_2) — An increased concentration of carbon dioxide in the blood of a dead person may indicate that they have suffocated — from choking, drowning, or inhalation of toxic gases.

Covalent Compounds Have Low Melting and Boiling Points

1) Covalent compounds usually exist as small molecules.

2) The atoms within the molecules share electrons.

3) The strong bonds formed when atoms share electrons are called covalent bonds.

4) In contrast, the forces of attraction between these molecules are very weak.

5) You only need a little bit of energy to overcome the weak forces between the molecules — so covalent compounds have low melting points and boiling points.

6) And this means they're usually gases and liquids at room temperature.

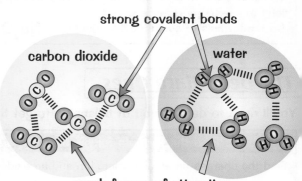

strong covalent bonds

carbon dioxide

water

weak forces of attraction

H₂O, CO₂, C₂H₅OH, DVD, FBI, GSOH...

Okay. So many substances obtained from living materials are organic. And organic compounds are joined together by covalent bonds. Got that? Now have a good look at the formulas of the covalent compounds — they'll expect you to know these. Cover up the page, scribble them down and check you've got them right.

Flame Tests and pH

Imagine the police are investigating a murder, and they've found a curious <u>white powder</u> near the blood-stained candlestick. It's time for the <u>forensic scientist</u> to start analysing the powder, maybe it's a clue...

Flame Tests <u>Test for</u> Metal Ions

<u>Flame tests</u> can identify which <u>metals</u>, if any, are present in a compound. If you put even <u>tiny</u> amounts of some metals into a flame, very distinctive <u>colours</u> can be seen.

To do a flame test you need a <u>nichrome wire loop</u>, dilute <u>hydrochloric acid</u> (HCl) and a blue <u>Bunsen flame</u>.

1) First make sure the nichrome wire loop is <u>really clean</u>, or you might <u>contaminate</u> your sample. Usually it's alright to dip the loop into <u>hydrochloric acid</u> and then rinse it in <u>distilled water</u>, but if it's really dirty you might have to use <u>emery cloth</u>.

2) <u>Dip</u> the wire in your sample (you only need a little).

3) Put the wire loop in the <u>blue</u> part of the <u>Bunsen flame</u> (the hottest bit).

4) <u>Observe</u> and <u>record</u> the results.

Compounds of some metals burn with a <u>characteristic colour</u>, as you see every November 5th. So, remember, remember...

1) <u>Sodium</u> ions, Na$^+$, burn with an <u>orange</u> flame.
2) <u>Potassium</u> ions, K$^+$, burn with a <u>lilac</u> flame.
3) <u>Calcium</u> ions, Ca^{2+}, burn with a <u>brick-red</u> flame.
4) <u>Copper</u> ions, Cu^{2+}, burn with a <u>blue-green</u> flame.

Universal Indicator Paper <u>and pH Meters</u> Measure pH

1) An indicator is just a dye that <u>changes colour</u> depending on whether it's <u>in an acid</u> or <u>in an alkali</u>. <u>Universal indicator</u> is a very useful <u>combination of dyes</u> which gives the colours shown below.

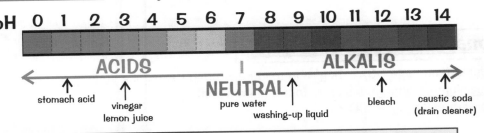

Universal indicator produces a range of different colours.

The pH scale goes from 0 to 14.

1) A <u>very strong acid</u> has <u>pH 0</u>. A <u>very strong alkali</u> has <u>pH 14</u>.
2) If something is <u>neutral</u> it has <u>pH 7</u> (e.g. pure water).
3) Anything <u>less</u> than 7 is <u>acidic</u>. Anything <u>more</u> than 7 is <u>alkaline</u>.

2) To measure the pH of a substance all you need to do is pipette a <u>drop</u> of it onto <u>universal indicator paper</u>, and record its <u>colour</u>. If it's a <u>solid sample</u> then you'll need to make it into a <u>solution</u> first (see page 60).

3) <u>pH meters</u> can also be used to measure the pH of a substance. These usually consist of a <u>probe</u>, which is dipped into the substance, and a <u>meter</u>, which gives a reading of the pH.

An untidy bedroom — the universal indicator for a teenager...

Using a pH meter is the most accurate method of measuring pH — it tells you the pH digitally so there's no messing about with trying to work out which colour the universal indicator paper resembles the most.

Solubility and Carbonates

With a little bit of this, and a little bit of that... you'll soon work out the identity of that mystery substance.

Finding the Solubility of a Sample

By finding out the solubility of a compound you can eliminate a lot of ionic compounds (see page 56).

And here's how to do it:

1) Add a very small amount of the substance to some distilled water in a boiling tube and shake.

2) After allowing it to settle, record what the contents look like.

3) If it's clear, the substance is soluble. If it's cloudy, it's slightly soluble, and if there's no change, it's insoluble.

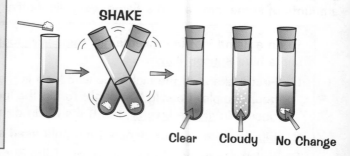

SHAKE

Clear   Cloudy   No Change

You've got to be very careful with this test — if you put in too much, the solution may become saturated, so it'll look like the soluble substance is insoluble.

A saturated solution is one that will not dissolve any more of the solid (unless you change the temperature).

Making a Soluble Sample into a Solution

For many chemical tests the substance needs to be in solution, like testing for pH (see page 59), and chromatography (see page 70).

Here's the method:

1) Add a spatula of the sample to some distilled water in a boiling tube and shake.

2) Repeat this process until no more solid will dissolve.

3) Pour the solution through some filter paper to remove any excess solid.

4) Store the solution for future testing.

Testing for Carbonates — Use Dilute Acid

Most carbonates are insoluble (see page 56). They're in many everyday items, like sodium carbonate, found in detergents, and calcium carbonate, which is found in antacids. All carbonates contain the carbonate ion — CO_3^{2-}.

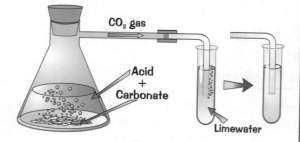

CO₂ gas

Acid + Carbonate

Limewater

Carbonates give off carbon dioxide when added to dilute acids. You can use this to test for CO_3^{2-} ions. Here's the method:

1) Put your mystery compound in dilute acid, e.g. dilute hydrochloric acid, and collect any gas given off.

2) Bubble the gas through limewater. If the limewater turns milky, the gas given off is carbon dioxide...

3) ...so your compound contains carbonate ions — CO_3^{2-}.

How soluble are you? Have a bath and see if you dissolve...

Illegal drugs, like heroin and cocaine, can be 'cut' or mixed with other white powders to increase their street value. These can include washing soda, which contains a carbonate. Other common ones are sugar, talcum powder and baby milk powder — it's amazing what stuff people will snort up their noses...

Precipitation Tests

In precipitation tests, two dissolved substances react to form an <u>insoluble</u> solid — called a <u>precipitate</u>. Precipitate tests can help you <u>identify</u> soluble ionic compounds. But first, a note on <u>word equations</u>...

Chemical Reactions are Shown Using Word Equations...

1) Word equations are an <u>easy</u> way to show what's going on in a reaction.

2) To <u>write a word equation</u> you just put the names of the <u>reactants</u> on the <u>left</u> of the arrow and the names of the <u>products</u> on the <u>right</u>.

3) For example, this is the reaction between <u>sodium</u> and <u>chlorine</u> to make <u>sodium chloride</u>:

sodium + chlorine → sodium chloride
reactants   product

Testing for Metal Ions — Sodium Hydroxide

1) Many <u>metal hydroxides</u> are <u>insoluble</u> — so they precipitate out of solution when formed.

2) Some of these hydroxides have a <u>characteristic colour</u>.

3) In this test you just add a few drops of <u>sodium hydroxide</u> solution to your mystery solution, and see what happens.

4) If a precipitate forms, its colour can tell you which <u>metal hydroxide</u> you've made — and so what the <u>metal bit</u> of your mystery compound could be...

Metal Ion	Colour of Precipitate
Calcium, Ca^{2+}	White
Copper, Cu^{2+}	Blue
Iron(II), Fe^{2+}	Sludgy Green
Iron(III), Fe^{3+}	Reddish Brown
Lead(II), Pb^{2+}	White at first. But if you add loads more NaOH it forms a colourless solution.

E.g. calcium chloride + sodium hydroxide → calcium hydroxide + sodium chloride

Testing for Sulfates — Hydrochloric Acid then Barium Chloride

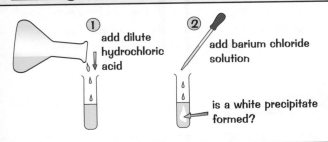

① add dilute hydrochloric acid

② add barium chloride solution

is a white precipitate formed?

1) Add some <u>dilute hydrochloric acid</u> to a solution of your compound.

2) Then add a few drops of <u>barium chloride solution</u> to the liquid.

3) If you see a <u>white precipitate</u>, there are <u>sulfate</u> ions (SO_4^{2-}) in your compound.

E.g. barium chloride + copper sulfate → barium sulfate + copper chloride

Testing for Chlorides — Nitric Acid then Silver Nitrate

1) Add <u>dilute nitric acid</u> to a solution of your compound.

2) Then add a few drops of <u>silver nitrate solution</u> to the liquid.

3) If you see a <u>white precipitate</u>, there are <u>chloride</u> ions (Cl^-) in your compound.

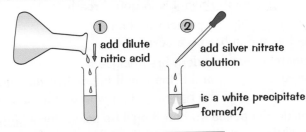

① add dilute nitric acid

② add silver nitrate solution

is a white precipitate formed?

E.g. silver nitrate + copper chloride → silver chloride + copper nitrate

Snow White Precipitate — and the Seven Analytical Chemists...

The coloured compound in each of the equations above shows the <u>insoluble product</u> (precipitate) of the reaction. You may be asked to <u>name</u> these — just swap over the first and second bits of the names of the reactants.

Testing for Ethanol

This next test involves an organic covalent compound. If you've forgotten what they are, have a quick flick back to page 58. I'm sure you'll be glad to hear that this is the last test in this section. Enjoy.

Use Acidified Potassium Dichromate to Test for Ethanol

It's illegal in the UK to 'drink and drive'. The amount of alcohol is measured using a breathalyser — which uses a chemical-based test to detect the presence of ethanol on a suspect's breath.

> 1) Acidified potassium dichromate solution is orange.
> 2) When ethanol is added the solution goes green.
> 3) This provides a simple colour change test to find out if a sample contains ethanol.
>
> orange → green

The Original Breathalyser Wasn't Very Accurate

The original breathalyser required police officers to decide if a suspect had passed or failed the test. This wasn't very accurate as it relied on each police officer's personal opinion. Here's how it worked:

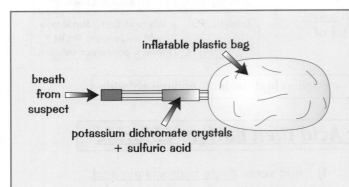

inflatable plastic bag

breath from suspect

potassium dichromate crystals + sulfuric acid

1) The suspect is asked to blow into the tube until the inflatable bag is full.

2) Potassium dichromate crystals are contained in a small chamber, mixed with sulfuric acid.

3) Any ethanol found in their breath will react with the potassium dichromate and turn it green.

4) The police officer then compares the colour with an unreacted sample — if the colour change is significant the suspect has failed the test.

Modern Breathalysers give a Digital Reading

1) Modern breathalysers use a similar test, but they give you a digital read-out of the amount of alcohol in your breath.

2) These breathalysers still contain acidified potassium dichromate but they work electronically.

3) Electronic sensors in the breathalyser detect the colour change if ethanol is in your breath.

4) The amount of ethanol present is then displayed as a number on a screen.

5) Unfortunately, even modern breathalysers aren't very accurate, and if the result is positive the suspect has to be taken into the police station where more accurate tests can be carried out.

6) Once inside the police station they'll be asked for a blood or urine sample so an analytical scientist can measure the alcohol concentration directly.

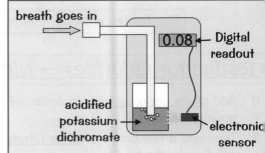

breath goes in

0.08 ← Digital readout

acidified potassium dichromate →

electronic sensor

Breathalysers — they analyse your breath... duh

Nowadays you don't get to breathe into a plastic bag — sad isn't it. Instead you have to blow into a grey box which digitally tells you how much alcohol there is in your breath. How boring is that? Ah well.

Identifying a Compound

A single chemical test isn't likely to identify a compound, so analytical scientists usually carry out a series of tests and the evidence from all of them is used to draw conclusions.

A Range of Different Tests Will Usually be Carried Out

EXAMPLE: A notorious drug dealer has been caught in possession of a large quantity of an unknown white powder, which is later identified as cocaine. Investigators would like to know what he used to cut the drug with, so that they can trace other drug samples back to the dealer.

They raid his house and find four different household white powders shown in the table.

Forensic scientists are given a sample of the powder and are asked to find out which household substance, if any, is present. Their final report is shown below.

Substance	Chemical Name	Chemical Formula
table salt	sodium chloride	$NaCl$
washing powder	sodium carbonate	Na_2CO_3
corn sugar	glucose	$C_6H_{12}O_6$
chalk	calcium carbonate	$CaCO_3$

Forensic Laboratory Report

PRIORITY: Urgent
DETAILS: White powder recovered from suspect. Check for possible match with substances retrieved from suspect's residence.

TEST	OBSERVATION	CONCLUSION
Solubility	Does dissolve	Sample is soluble in water.
pH	pH 9	Sample is slightly alkaline.
Flame Test	Orange flame	Sample contains sodium.
Precipitation (with nitric acid and silver nitrate)	No white precipitate	Sample doesn't contain chloride ions.
Carbonate Test	Limewater turned cloudy	Sample contains a carbonate.

CONCLUSION: The white powder is likely to contain sodium carbonate, which is commonly found in washing powder.

Signature: Date: 14 / 06 / 2012

Scientists Try to Make Their Results Accurate and Reproducible

1) To make the results of a chemical test more reliable, the test should be repeated at least once by a different scientist.

2) The sample should also be kept free from contamination.

3) Scientists can collect more accurate results by using more sensitive equipment, like mass spectrometry and chromatography (see pages 70 & 76).

4) To make sure their results are reproducible, scientists must follow standard procedures or make a detailed record of their experimental methods.

There's more on accurate and reliable results on page 86.

Sherlock Holmes never looked so good in a lab coat...

So if you ever come across a suspicious white powder, you'll know what to do...

Balancing Equations

Sometimes, analytical scientists need to use balanced equations to show what's happening in a reaction.

Symbol Equations Show What Happens in Chemical Reactions

Balanced symbol equations show the atoms at the start (the reactant atoms) and the atoms at the end (the product atoms) of a reaction and how they're arranged. For example:

> Word equation: magnesium + oxygen → magnesium oxide
>
> Balanced symbol equation: $2Mg$ + O_2 → $2MgO$

Balancing the Equation — Match Them Up One by One

1) There must always be the same number of atoms of each element on both sides — they can't just disappear.

2) You balance the equation by putting numbers in front of the formulas where needed. Take this equation for reacting sulfuric acid (H_2SO_4) with sodium hydroxide (NaOH) to get sodium sulfate (Na_2SO_4) and water (H_2O):

$$H_2SO_4 + NaOH \rightarrow Na_2SO_4 + H_2O$$

The formulas are all correct but the numbers of some atoms don't match up on both sides. E.g. there are 3 Hs on the left, but only 2 on the right. You can't change formulas like H_2O to H_3O. You can only put numbers in front of them.

Method: Balance Just ONE Type of Atom at a Time

The more you practise, the quicker you get, but all you do is this:

1) Find an element that doesn't balance and pencil in a number to try and sort it out.

2) See where it gets you. It may create another imbalance — if so, just pencil in another number and see where that gets you.

3) Carry on chasing unbalanced elements and it'll sort itself out pretty quickly.

I'll show you. In the equation above you soon notice we're short of H atoms on the RHS (Right-Hand Side).

1) The only thing you can do about that is make it $2H_2O$ instead of just H_2O:

$$H_2SO_4 + NaOH \rightarrow Na_2SO_4 + 2H_2O$$

2) But that now causes too many H atoms and O atoms on the RHS, so to balance that up you could try putting 2NaOH on the LHS (Left-Hand Side):

$$H_2SO_4 + 2NaOH \rightarrow Na_2SO_4 + 2H_2O$$

3) And suddenly there it is! Everything balances. And you'll notice the Na just sorted itself out.

Balancing equations — weigh it up in your mind...

REMEMBER WHAT THOSE NUMBERS MEAN: A number in front of a formula applies to the entire formula. So, $3Na_2SO_4$ means three lots of Na_2SO_4. The little numbers in the middle or at the end of a formula only apply to the atom or brackets immediately before. So the 4 in Na_2SO_4 just means 4 Os, not 4 Ss.

Revision Summary for Section 6

My favourite part of any section — the end. But it's not over yet — there's still this beautiful revision summary to get through. You've covered ionic and covalent compounds and a handful of tests which you need to be able to describe. If your memory fails you, then have a look back through the section.

1) Name one type of analytical scientist and explain what they do.

2) Give two things that determine the characteristics of a substance.

3) What type of structure do ionic compounds have?

4) Explain why ionic compounds are usually solids at room temperature.

5) Are the following ionic compounds soluble in water? a) potassium nitrate, b) lead sulfate, c) ammonium chloride, d) sodium hydroxide, e) calcium carbonate.

6)* Use the table to help you find the formula for:
   a) iron(II) oxide,   b) iron(III) oxide,
   c) calcium chloride, d) sodium carbonate.

Positive ions		Negative ions	
sodium	Na^+	chloride	Cl^-
calcium	Ca^{2+}	oxide	O^{2-}
iron(II)	Fe^{2+}	carbonate	CO_3^{2-}
iron(III)	Fe^{3+}		

7) Do organic compounds tend to have ionic or covalent bonding?

8) Give the formulas of the following compounds: a) carbon dioxide, b) ethanol, c) glucose.

9) What do the atoms within a molecule of a covalent compound share?

10) Explain why covalent substances are usually gases or liquids at room temperature.

11) Describe how to carry out a flame test.

12) What ions are present in these flame tests: a) lilac flame? b) blue-green flame?

13) What is universal indicator?

14) A substance was found to have a pH of 5. Is it an acid or an alkali?

15) Describe how you could test to see if a compound is soluble in water.

16) Describe how you could make a solution from a solid sample (that's soluble in water).

17) What gas is released when a carbonate is placed into some dilute acid?
    How could you test for this gas?

18) Describe how you could distinguish between solutions of: a) calcium sulfate and copper sulfate, b) copper nitrate and copper sulfate, c) sodium chloride and sodium hydroxide.

19)* Name the products that are formed during each of the following reactions:
    a) barium chloride + iron(II) sulfate, b) silver nitrate + zinc chloride

20) What colour change occurs when ethanol is passed over crystals of acidified potassium dichromate?

21) Describe the original breathalyser, and suggest why it isn't very accurate.

22)* Forensic scientists are investigating the identity of an unknown white solid.
    They conduct a series of chemical tests and obtain the following results:
    • soluble in water,
    • produces a blue precipitate with sodium hydroxide solution,
    • produces a white precipitate with barium chloride solution (after first adding dilute HCl).
    a) Name the white solid.
    b) Give the formula of this compound.

23)* Balance these equations:
    a) $CaCO_3 + HCl \rightarrow CaCl_2 + H_2O + CO_2$
    b) $Ca + H_2O \rightarrow Ca(OH)_2 + H_2$

* Answers on page 92.

Section 6 — Chemical Analysis

Relative Formula Mass

The biggest trouble with <u>relative formula mass</u> is that it <u>sounds</u> a lot worse than it really is.

Relative Atomic Mass, A_r — *Easy Peasy*

1) This is just a way of saying how <u>heavy</u> different atoms are <u>compared</u> with the mass of an atom of carbon-12. Carbon-12 has A_r of <u>exactly 12</u>.

2) In the <u>Periodic table</u>, the elements all have <u>two</u> numbers next to them. The <u>bigger</u> number is the <u>relative atomic mass</u>.

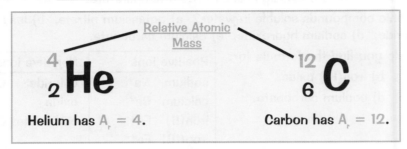

<u>Relative Atomic Mass</u>

$$^4_2\text{He}$$

Helium has $A_r = 4$.

$$^{12}_6\text{C}$$

Carbon has $A_r = 12$.

Relative Formula Mass, M_r — *Also Easy Peasy*

If you have a compound like $MgCl_2$ then it has a <u>relative formula mass</u>, M_r, which is just all the relative atomic masses <u>added together</u>.
For $MgCl_2$ it would be:

The relative atomic mass of chlorine is multiplied by 2 because there are two chlorine atoms.

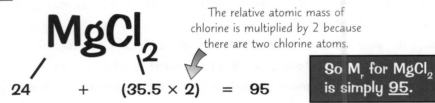

$$\text{MgCl}_2$$

$$24 \quad + \quad (35.5 \times 2) \quad = \quad 95$$

So M_r for $MgCl_2$ is simply <u>95</u>.

In the exam, you'll be <u>given</u> the relative atomic masses in the question if you need them. And that's all it is. A big fancy name like <u>relative formula mass</u> and all it means is "<u>add up all the relative atomic masses</u>". What a swizz, eh?

"ONE MOLE" of a Substance is Equal to its M_r *or* A_r *in Grams*

The <u>relative formula mass</u> (M_r) or <u>relative atomic mass</u> (A_r) of a substance <u>in grams</u> is known as <u>one mole</u> of that substance.

<u>Examples</u>:

Iron, Fe, has an A_r of 56.

Nitrogen gas, N_2, has an M_r of 28 (2×14).

Potassium chloride, KCl, has an M_r of 74.5 ($39 + 35.5$).

So one mole of iron weighs exactly 56 g

So one mole of N_2 weighs exactly 28 g

So one mole of KCl weighs exactly 74.5 g

Numbers? — and you thought you were doing applied science...

Read through the stuff on this page about how to work out <u>relative formula mass</u>. Then, have a go at these:
Find the relative formula mass of: NaOH, Fe_2O_3, C_6H_{14}*
Here are the relative atomic masses: Na=23, O=16, Fe=56, C=12, H=1.

Calculating Masses in Reactions

You can calculate the masses of the reactants or products in a reaction using a balanced symbol equation.

The Three Important Steps — Not to Be Missed...

(Miss one out and it'll all go horribly wrong, believe me.)

> 1) Take the balanced symbol equation.
> 2) Work out M_r — just for the two bits you want
> 3) Apply the rule: Divide to get one, then multiply to get all
>   (But you have to apply this first to the substance they
>   give you information about, and then the other one!)

Don't worry — these steps should all make sense when you look at the example below.

Example: What mass of magnesium oxide is produced when 60 g of magnesium is burned in air?
The balanced equation for this reaction is $2Mg + O_2 \rightarrow 2MgO$.

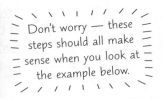
Higher tier students only — if you haven't been given the balanced symbol equation, you'll need to write it out yourself. See page 64 for more.

Answer:

1) Take the balanced equation: $\implies$ $2Mg + O_2 \rightarrow 2MgO$

2) Work out the relative formula masses: $\implies$ $2 \times 24 \rightarrow 2 \times (24+16)$
   (don't do the oxygen — we don't need it) $\qquad 48 \qquad \rightarrow \qquad 80$

3) Apply the rule: Divide to get one, then multiply to get all:
   The two numbers, 48 and 80, tell us that 48 g of Mg react to give 80 g of MgO.
   Here's the tricky bit. You've now got to be able to write this down:

> 48 g of Mg ......reacts to give.....80 g of MgO
>
> 1 g of Mg ......reacts to give.....
>
> 60 g of Mg .....reacts to give......

The big clue is that in the question they've said we want to burn "60 g of magnesium",
i.e. they've told us how much magnesium to have, and that's how you know to write down the
left-hand side of it first, because:

> We'll first need to ÷ by 48 to get 1 g of Mg
> and then need to × by 60 to get 60 g of Mg.

Then you can work out the numbers on the other side (shown in purple below) by realising that you must
divide both sides by 48 and then multiply both sides by 60. It's tricky.

$$\div 48 \begin{cases} 48 \text{ g of Mg} \ldots\ldots\ldots 80 \text{ g of MgO} \\ 1 \text{ g of Mg} \ldots\ldots\ldots 1.67 \text{ g of MgO} \\ 60 \text{ g of Mg} \ldots\ldots\ldots 100 \text{ g of MgO} \end{cases} \div 48 \atop \times 60$$

$\times 60$

This finally tells us that 60 g of magnesium will produce 100 g of magnesium oxide.
If the question had said "Find how much magnesium gives 500 g of magnesium oxide", you'd fill in the
MgO side first, because that's the one you'd have the information about. Got it? Good-O!

Reaction mass calculations — no worries, matey...

The only way to get good at these is to practise. So have a go at this one:
Find the mass of calcium which gives 30 g of calcium oxide (CaO) when burnt in air.
The balanced equation is: $Ca + \frac{1}{2}O_2 \rightarrow CaO$, the relative atomic masses are: Ca = 40, O = 16.*

* Answers on page 92.

Titrations

Titrations are used to determine the <u>amount</u> of a <u>substance</u> in a <u>sample</u>, which is <u>useful</u> for all kinds of things

You Can Test for Acidity Using Titrations

<u>Titrations</u> are used by scientists for many <u>different things</u>. For example:

- <u>Environmental scientists</u> use titrations to determine the amount of acid in <u>rain water</u> or to test for certain <u>metal ions</u> in <u>polluted river water</u>.
- <u>Food scientists</u> use titrations to test the concentration of <u>acid</u> in <u>vinegar</u>, or <u>lactic acid</u> in <u>milk</u>.

You Need to Know How to Do an Acid-Base Titration

You can carry out <u>acid-base titrations</u> to find out the <u>amount</u> (concentration) of <u>acid</u> in a solution, e.g. the amount of ethanoic acid in vinegar. You'll find out what to do with your <u>results</u> on the next page, but for now, here's <u>how</u> to do the <u>titration</u>.

1) Measure some of your sample solution into a <u>titration flask</u>.

2) Then add two or three drops of <u>indicator</u>.

3) Fill a <u>burette</u> with a known concentration of alkali — then take a reading by writing down <u>how much alkali</u> is in the burette.

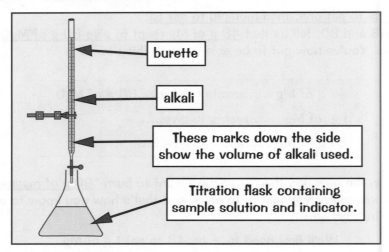

4) Using the <u>burette</u>, add the <u>alkali</u> to your sample a bit at a time. Keep giving the titration flask a <u>swirl</u> to help <u>mix</u> the solutions.

- The <u>end point</u> of the titration is when <u>all</u> the acid in the sample has been <u>neutralised</u> by the alkali.
- This will cause the indicator in the flask to <u>change colour</u>.

5) You need to go <u>slow</u> when you think the <u>end point</u> is about to be reached.

6) When you reach the end point and the indicator changes colour, <u>stop</u> adding the alkali. Then <u>write down</u> the <u>final volume</u> of alkali in the burette.

7) You can work out the <u>volume of alkali</u> used to neutralise the acid by calculating the <u>difference</u> between the <u>first</u> and <u>final</u> reading of the burette.

You can also use acid-base titrations to find the concentration of alkali in a solution — you just need to add an acid with a known concentration to your sample.

Acids are always in trouble — they just keep getting dropped in it...

Titrations aren't too tricky really — you just need to make sure your results are <u>accurate</u>, which means <u>going slowly near the end-point</u>. Oh, and don't forget the indicator — you'll be waiting a long time without it.

Titrations

So now you know how do to a titration (see previous page). Next up, how to use the results of your titration to calculate the amount of substance in a sample, e.g. the concentration of acid in a solution...

The Calculation — Work Out the Number of Moles

Now for the calculations... basically, you're trying to find the number of moles of each substance. A formula triangle is pretty handy here, I reckon:

If you can't remember what moles are, flick back to page 66.

$$\text{Mole-concentration} = \frac{\text{Number of Moles}}{\text{Volume (dm}^3)}$$

See the inside front cover for how to use formula triangles.

Example — Working out the concentration of ethanoic acid in vinegar

Matt has 25 cm³ of vinegar containing an unknown concentration of ethanoic acid (CH_3COOH) in his flask.

He does a titration and finds that it takes 30 cm³ of sodium hydroxide (NaOH) to neutralise the acid in the vinegar.

The sodium hydroxide has a concentration of 1 mol per dm³.

Find the concentration of ethanoic acid in the vinegar.

Step 1: Work out how many moles of the 'known' substance you have:

Using the formula triangle, you can see that:

Number of moles = concentration × volume

$= 1 × (30 / 1000) = \underline{0.03 \text{ moles}}$

In this case, the known substance is NaOH.

This is to get a volume in dm³, rather than cm³
(30 cm³ / 1000 = 0.03 dm³)

You need to be able to write out word equations for titrations. See page 61 for how to do this. Higher tier students also need to be able to write balanced symbol equations — see page 64.

Step 2: Write down the balanced equation for the reaction...

$$CH_3COOH + NaOH \longrightarrow CH_3COONa + H_2O$$

...and work out how many moles of the 'unknown' stuff you must have had.

Using the equation, you can see that for every mole of sodium hydroxide you had...
...there was one mole of ethanoic acid.

So if you had 0.03 moles of sodium hydroxide...
...you must have had 0.03 moles of ethanoic acid.

Step 3: Work out the concentration of the 'unknown' stuff.

Concentration = number of moles ÷ volume

$= 0.03 ÷ (25 / 1000) = \underline{1.2 \text{ moles per dm}^3}$

So the concentration of ethanoic acid in vinegar is 1.2 mols per dm³.

To get dm³ again.

HOW SCIENCE WORKS

Repeating the titration and calculating the average of your results increases the reliability of your experiment. See page 86 for more information on reliability.

Titrations — just lather, rinse and repeat...

..oh wait — that's shampooing your hair. But the repeating bit is really important in titrations too. Doing the experiment a few times helps to make sure your results are reliable. If you get the same result a number of times, you can have more faith in it than if it's a one-off (it's just a shame it doesn't give you glossy hair too).

Chromatography

Chromatography is used a lot in the chemical industry — it's a <u>method</u> for <u>separating chemical mixtures</u>.

Chromatography Can be Used to Detect Forgeries

1) Chromatography can be used to <u>analyse</u> loads of different <u>unknown mixtures</u>.

2) For example, it can be used to analyse the <u>inks</u> used in a <u>suspected forgery</u> (faked document).

3) Most inks are made up of a mixture of dyes. A forged document will probably use <u>different ink</u> from an <u>official document</u> (so it'll contain a different mixture of dyes).

There are <u>two types</u> of chromatography you need to know about:

1. Paper Chromatography

Here's how you do <u>paper chromatography</u>...

1) Draw a <u>line</u> across the bottom of a sheet of <u>filter paper</u>. Pencil is used because the pencil marks are <u>insoluble</u> and won't be separated by the solvent.

2) Add <u>spots of ink</u> to the line at regular intervals.

3) Tape the top of the paper to a pencil and <u>hang</u> the sheet in a <u>beaker of solvent</u>, e.g. <u>water</u>.

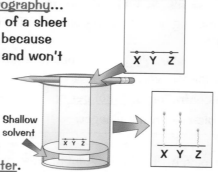

Shallow solvent

4) The <u>solvent</u> used depends on what's being tested. Some compounds <u>dissolve</u> well in <u>water</u>, but sometimes other (<u>non-aqueous</u>) solvents, like ethanol, need to be used.

5) The solvent <u>seeps</u> up the paper, carrying the ink dyes with it.

6) Each different dye will move up the paper at a <u>different rate</u> and form a <u>spot</u> in a different place.

2. Thin-Layer Chromatography (TLC)

1) This technique is very <u>similar</u> to paper chromatography.

2) The main difference is that instead of paper it uses a <u>thin layer of gel or paste</u> (e.g. silica gel) on a <u>glass plate</u>.

3) This allows a wide range of <u>non-aqueous</u> solvents to be used, e.g. ethanol, acetone, etc.

Chromatography Works Because Different Dyes Move at Different Rates

1) In both types of chromatography the dyes are separated by the movement of a <u>solvent</u> (called the <u>mobile phase</u>) through a <u>medium</u> of filter paper or gel (called the <u>stationary phase</u>).

2) The dyes move <u>between</u> the <u>mobile</u> and <u>stationary phases</u> as they move up the medium.

3) The different dyes move up at <u>different rates</u> because they have <u>different solubilities</u>.

4) This means that they travel <u>different distances</u> up the medium.

5) The <u>more soluble</u> dyes spend more time in the mobile phase and so move up the paper (or gel) <u>faster</u> than the less soluble ones, which spend more time in the stationary phase.

6) This means that the more soluble dyes travel <u>further</u> than the less soluble ones.

more soluble

less soluble

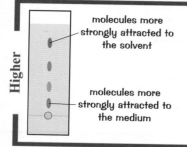

Higher

molecules more strongly attracted to the solvent

molecules more strongly attracted to the medium

7) The <u>speed</u> that a dye moves up the medium depends on whether the <u>molecules</u> in the <u>dye</u> are more strongly attracted to the <u>molecules</u> in the <u>solvent</u> or the <u>molecules</u> in the <u>stationary phase</u> (the filter paper or gel).

8) If the molecules in the dye are <u>more</u> strongly attracted to the molecules in the <u>medium</u>, the dye will move at a <u>slower</u> rate than it would if they were more strongly attracted to the molecules in the solvent.

So don't try forging your parent's signature to get out of gym class...

...<u>chromatography</u> will <u>catch you out</u>. All your PE teacher needs is a beaker of water and your pen so watch out.

Analysing Chromatograms

The previous page was all about chromatography. The pattern of spots you get from a chromatography experiment is called a chromatogram. This page is all about interpreting chromatograms — they're more than just a load of pretty dots you know...

Unknown Compounds are Compared to Reference Materials

1) If you want to work out the mixture of dyes in an unknown ink, you first need to do a chromatography analysis of the ink (see previous page).

2) Once you've got your chromatogram, you can compare the dyes in the unknown ink to the dyes in known inks (reference materials) to see which ink it is.

3) The pattern of dye spots will match when two inks are the same.

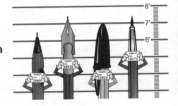

EXAMPLE:

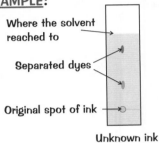  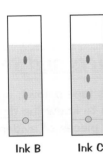 

Where the solvent reached to

Separated dyes

Original spot of ink

Unknown ink   Ink A   Ink B   Ink C   Ink D

You can see from the position of the spots on the filter paper that the unknown ink has the same composition as ink B.

You can Calculate the R_f Value for Each Unknown Substance

1) You can work out the R_f values for spots (the unknown substances) on a chromatogram.

2) An R_f value is the ratio between the distance travelled by the unknown substance and the distance travelled by the solvent. You can find R_f values using the formula:

R_f values are always between 0 and 1, so make sure that your answer is too.

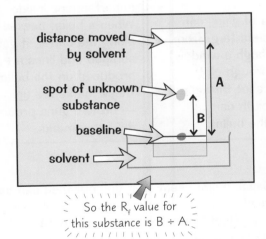

distance moved by solvent

spot of unknown substance

baseline

solvent

So the R_f value for this substance is B ÷ A.

$$R_f = \frac{\text{distance travelled by substance}}{\text{distance travelled by solvent}}$$

EXAMPLE:
- The diagram shows a chromatography analysis of an ink.
- The solvent travelled 8 cm.
- The dye from the ink travelled 2 cm.
- Calculate the R_f value of the dye.

$$R_f = \frac{\text{distance travelled by substance}}{\text{distance travelled by solvent}}$$

$$R_f = \frac{2 \text{ cm}}{8 \text{ cm}} = 0.25$$

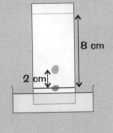

3) If the R_f values of two samples match, the substances may be the same (although it doesn't definitely prove they are the same).

4) If the R_f values of two samples are different, then the samples contain different substances.

Comb-atography — identifies mysterious things in your hair...

Chromatography works by showing how mystery chemicals get distributed between mobile and stationary phases — that's what the R_f value represents. You can use the R_f values and the pattern of spots on the chromatogram to identify the chemical. It's clever stuff. Give it a go yourself — it's a really simple experiment to do.

Comparison Microscopes

Loads of <u>clever equipment</u> has been developed which allows <u>analytical scientists</u> to <u>compare and analyse</u> <u>samples</u>. This sort of stuff is really useful when it comes to solving crimes. For instance, some pieces of evidence are <u>way too small</u> to look at and analyse with the naked eye, which is where <u>microscopes</u> come in.

A <u>Comparison</u> **Microscope is Used to** <u>Compare Things</u>

1) A comparison microscope is a bit like <u>two light microscopes</u> (like you'd use at school) <u>stuck together</u>.

2) They allow you to see two bits of evidence <u>next to each other</u> so you can compare them.

3) This photo shows a forensic scientist using a comparison microscope to <u>compare bullets</u>.

MAURO FERMARIELLO / SCIENCE PHOTO LIBRARY

They're Used to Compare <u>Bullets</u> and <u>Seeds</u>

They're good for looking at <u>bullets</u> and <u>seeds</u> (see below), and also for looking at <u>fibres</u> and <u>soil</u> (see next page). You need to know the <u>distinctive features</u> that allow forensic scientists to <u>match</u> these pieces of evidence.

BULLETS

1) Bullets are sometimes found at the scenes of <u>violent crimes</u>.

2) They're useful in forensics because fired bullets are <u>unique</u> to <u>one gun</u>.

3) If you find a gun you can fire a <u>test bullet</u> and <u>compare</u> it to the bullet found at the crime scene.

4) If they match, then you can <u>match the gun to the crime</u>.

5) If you can then <u>match a person to the gun</u> you've found a possible <u>suspect</u>. Genius.

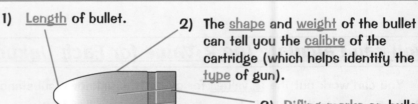

1) <u>Length</u> of bullet.

2) The <u>shape</u> and <u>weight</u> of the bullet can tell you the <u>calibre</u> of the cartridge (which helps identify the <u>type</u> of gun).

3) <u>Rifling marks</u> on bullet. Gun barrels have tiny imperfections inside. When a bullet passes along the barrel, it gets scraped and lines are produced on the bullet. These marks are <u>unique</u> — no two guns produc[e] the same marks.

4) <u>Other objects</u>. Bits of <u>glass</u> can be embedded in bullets (e.g. from the bullet going through a window). If the bullet goes through <u>cloth</u> (e.g. if someone is shot through their clothing) the cloth can <u>leave a pattern</u> on the bullet.

SEEDS

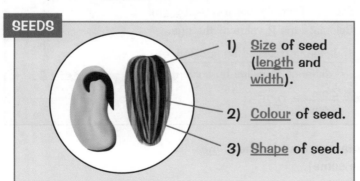

1) <u>Size</u> of seed (<u>length</u> and <u>width</u>).

2) <u>Colour</u> of seed.

3) <u>Shape</u> of seed.

1) Seeds might seem a <u>bit dull</u> but they can be used to show <u>where</u> objects or people <u>have been</u> (just like pollen can — see p.74).

2) This information can be used to <u>back up alibis</u>, or <u>link</u> people or objects to <u>crime scenes</u>, e.g. if the same seeds that are present at the crime scene are found on a suspect's trousers then there may be a link.

Comparison microscopes — mine's bigger than yours...

Thanks to <u>modern analytical techniques</u>, solving crimes has become a lot <u>easier</u>. Comparison microscopes are just one example — analytical scientists have all kinds of <u>special equipment</u> that they can use to <u>analyse sampl[es]</u> from crime scenes. Intrigued... then read on — this stuff would certainly put Sherlock Holmes out of a job.

Polarising Microscopes

Sometimes a light microscope <u>doesn't show up everything</u>. Analytical scientists can use a nifty bit of equipment called a <u>polarising microscope</u> to reveal more...

Polarising *Microscopes are a Bit Different*

1) Polarising microscopes are <u>kinda complicated</u>, but luckily you don't need to know how they work.
2) They're used because they <u>let you see things</u> that you <u>can't see</u> using a <u>light microscope</u>.
3) Analytical scientists will still use a comparison microscope too, but polarising microscopes can help reveal <u>extra details</u> about a sample.

They're Good For Looking at *Fibres...*

1) Fibres are <u>found</u> at all sorts of <u>different crime scenes</u>, e.g. a few fibres from a burglar's jacket on a broken window, a human hair from an attacker on a victim's shirt etc.
2) Fibres <u>aren't usually unique</u>, but they can still be used to <u>link</u> a suspect (or their clothing, or belongings) to a crime scene.
3) The sort of fibres forensic scientists might look at are human hairs, animal hairs, clothing fibres and carpet fibres.
4) Using a <u>polarising</u> microscope lets you see <u>man-made fibres</u> much more clearly:

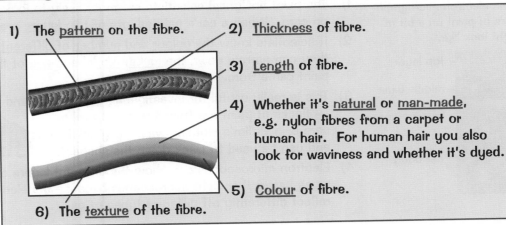

1) The <u>pattern</u> on the fibre.
2) <u>Thickness</u> of fibre.
3) <u>Length</u> of fibre.
4) Whether it's <u>natural</u> or <u>man-made</u>, e.g. nylon fibres from a carpet or human hair. For human hair you also look for waviness and whether it's dyed.
5) <u>Colour</u> of fibre.
6) The <u>texture</u> of the fibre.

...and Soil

Analytical scientists look at:

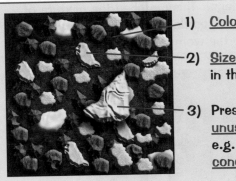

1) <u>Colour</u> of soil.
2) <u>Size of particles</u> in the soil.
3) Presence of <u>unusual materials</u>, e.g. bits of <u>concrete</u> or <u>glass</u>.

1) Soil is made up of <u>minerals</u>, bits of <u>rock</u>, <u>organic matter</u> (e.g. dead leaves and worms) and <u>water</u>.
2) Soil <u>composition varies</u> a lot from place to place. This makes it pretty useful evidence because it can show <u>where</u> something has been, e.g. soil on a suspect's shoe could be linked to a muddy crime scene.
3) Using a <u>polarising</u> microscope makes it easier to see things like <u>glass fragments</u> and <u>minerals</u> in the soil sample.

How do you polarise a microscope? Take it to the Arctic...

Sorry... lame joke. Anyway, fibres and soil, hmmm... they're not the most thrilling things in the world but they can provide <u>strong evidence</u> of a link between a suspect and a crime scene. Just think — your muddy shoes could prove you've been down the park when you were supposed to be in bed. Unlucky for you if your mum's a forensic scientist.

Electron Microscopes

Some distinctive features are <u>too small</u> to even see on a polarising microscope (they're really, really, really small) — when this is the case scientists use <u>electron microscopes</u>...

Electron Microscopes are Very Powerful

1) Electron microscopes use a <u>beam of electrons</u> to <u>produce an image</u> of the sample on a computer screen
2) They can <u>magnify</u> images many more times than light microscopes, so they can show <u>more detail</u>.

They're Good for Looking at Fibres...

Electron microscopes show <u>lots of detail</u>, so you can see the <u>pattern</u> and <u>texture</u> of different fibre types in <u>even greater detail</u> than with a polarising microscope.

EXAMPLE As this <u>electron micrograph</u> shows, <u>wool</u> has a pattern of <u>surface scales</u>, whereas <u>silk</u> has a <u>smooth surface</u>.

— silk

— wool

EYE OF SCIENCE / SCIENCE PHOTO LIBRARY

Most synthetic fibres have smooth surfaces too.

...And Layers of Paint...

This is what an electron micrograph of three layers of paint on a bit of car body might look like.

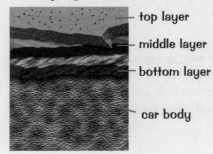

— top layer
— middle layer
— bottom layer
— car body

1) The paint analytical scientists are most likely to look at is the paint on <u>cars</u>. When a car's painted <u>lots</u> of <u>thin layers</u> are applied.
2) If scientists know the <u>colour</u> and <u>number</u> of <u>different layers</u> then they can narrow down the <u>make</u>, <u>model</u> and <u>age</u> of the car the paint came from.
3) This is really useful for investigating <u>car crashes</u> and <u>hit-and-runs</u> — flecks of paint are transferred onto other cars or a victim's clothing when they hit them and can be used to track down the suspect.
4) Electron microscopes can show the different layers of paint <u>much better</u> than light microscopes because the electrons reflect differently off <u>different types of paint</u>.

...And Pollen Grains

1) Pollen grains can tell you a lot about <u>where</u> an object or person has <u>been</u> because <u>different pollens</u> are found in <u>different areas</u>. This can help to do loads of things like <u>link</u> suspects to a crime scene or figure out which country things like counterfeit money have come from.

For example, a woman was arrested for suspected arson. Forensic scientists found a mixture of pollens on her trouser legs. This matched the mixture of pollens in the back garden of the house that burnt down — linking the woman to the crime scene.

2) When analytical scientists are comparing pollens they look at the <u>size</u>, <u>shape</u> and <u>surface pattern</u> of pollen grains. Each <u>type</u> of plant has <u>distinctive pollen</u>.
3) Electron microscopes are used to look at pollen grains because they're <u>really small</u> (around a tenth of a millimetre). Also, electron microscopes can give a more <u>detailed image</u> of the <u>pollen surface</u>.

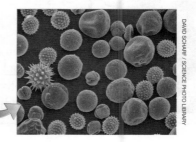

DAVID SCHARF / SCIENCE PHOTO LIBRARY

I think I prefer layers of cake, to be honest...

Paint layers on cars usually <u>aren't unique</u> (but they can be if the car has been custom painted).
Pollen grains are unique to each plant, so identifying a mixture of pollens can be really useful.

Instrumental Methods

I'm afraid this page has nothing to do with learning to play the guitar. Sorry. Instrumental methods means using machines to do the donkey work of identifying substances, rather than using traditional lab methods.

Instrumental Methods are Precise and Reliable

1) Lab methods are the traditional analytical tests that chemists use to test samples, e.g. titrations.

2) Advances in electronics and computing has led to the development of instrumental methods — using machines to identify substances, rather than the traditional lab methods.

3) The development of instrumental methods has made more advanced analysis possible.

4) This is useful for medical purposes, police forensic work, environmental analysis, checking whether an athlete has taken a banned substance, analysis of products in industry, and so on...

Advantages of Using Instrumental Methods

- Machines can be operated by technicians. Lab methods need trained chemists to do everything.

- Instrumental techniques are more reliable — using machines removes the possibility of human error.

- Instrumental techniques are more precise than traditional lab methods. This is because the instruments used are more accurate and can detect the tiniest amounts of substances.

- Instrumental techniques are much faster than lab methods, and tests can be automated (controlled by machines).

For more on precision and reliability, see page 86.

Disadvantages of Using Instrumental Methods

- It's very expensive to buy, run and maintain the machines.

Examples of Instrumental Methods Include...

1. Gas-Liquid Chromatography (GLC)

1) This uses a similar principle to paper or TLC chromatography (see page 70).

2) It's used to identify substances in a mixture.

HOW IT WORKS

1) A detector produces a chromatogram, which shows a series of peaks.

2) Each peak represents a different substance in the mixture.

3) Different substances have different retention times. (This is how long it takes a substance to pass through the GLC equipment).

4) You can compare the chromatogram of an unknown mixture to those of known mixtures to work out what it is.

5) For example:

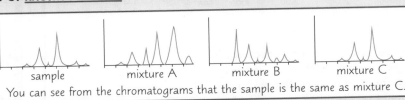

sample   mixture A   mixture B   mixture C

You can see from the chromatograms that the sample is the same as mixture C.

That's not all folks...

...there are more examples of instrumental methods on the next page. Woo-hoo. I know it's not exactly the most exciting stuff, and it can be a bit tricky, but you've got to know it. Got it. Cool. Then read on...

Instrumental Methods

2. Mass Spectrometry

1) You can work out the mass of the molecules in a substance using a mass spectrometer.

2) Electrons are fired at a sample. This causes the molecules to break up into fragments (ions).

3) The fragments are recorded on a mass spectrum, giving a fragmentation pattern.

4) This pattern allows analytical scientists to work out what the unknown sample is.

EXAMPLE:

1) The formula for pentane is $CH_3CH_2CH_2CH_2CH_3$. Below is the mass spectrum of pentane:

2) Each peak on the mass spectrum is caused by a different fragment ion, e.g. CH_3^+, $CH_3CH_2^+$, etc.

3) From looking at the fragmentation pattern, analytical scientists are able to work out that the unknown substance is pentane. Clever stuff.

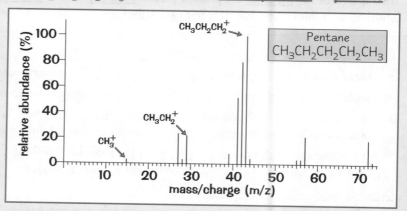

Pentane
$CH_3CH_2CH_2CH_2CH_3$

$CH_3CH_2CH_2^+$

$CH_3CH_2^+$

CH_3^+

relative abundance (%)

mass/charge (m/z)

3. Infrared (IR) Spectrometry

1) This technique can be used to identify the chemicals in solids, liquids or gases.

2) Infrared radiation is passed through a sample.

3) The frequencies of radiation that are absorbed are recorded on an infrared spectrum.

4) The infrared spectrum for each compound is unique.

5) This means an unknown sample can be identified by comparing its infrared spectrum with reference spectrums.

> Infrared radiation is a wavelength of light that is not visible to the naked eye.

EXAMPLE:

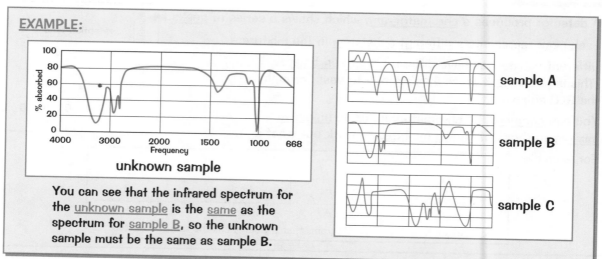

% absorbed

Frequency

unknown sample

You can see that the infrared spectrum for the unknown sample is the same as the spectrum for sample B, so the unknown sample must be the same as sample B.

sample A

sample B

sample C

Unfortunately, machines can't do the exam for you...

Luckily, you aren't expected to know the details of how these machines work. What you do need to know is how analytical scientists are able to use these techniques to work out what an unknown substance is.

Blood Group Typing

Blood is often found at the scenes of <u>violent</u> crimes, e.g. murders and assaults, hmmm... gruesome. <u>Blood typing</u> can tell forensic scientists whether a blood sample is <u>human</u> and which <u>blood group</u> it is. The blood group can then be <u>compared</u> to the <u>suspect's</u> to see if they <u>match</u>.

Blood Contains Four Main Things

1) Red Blood Cells

They <u>carry oxygen</u> to all the cells in the body. They make the blood look <u>red</u>.

2) White Blood Cells

Their main role is <u>defence against disease</u>.

nucleus — cell membrane — cytoplasm — cell membrane

3) Platelets

These are small fragments of cells that help the <u>blood to clot</u>.

4) Plasma

This is the <u>liquid</u> that <u>carries</u> everything about.

<u>Animal cells</u> like <u>white blood cells</u> are surrounded by a thin layer called a <u>cell membrane</u>. They are filled with a jelly-like substance called <u>cytoplasm</u> and contain a <u>nucleus</u>.

There are Four Main Blood Groups

1) People have different <u>blood groups</u> (sometimes called blood <u>types</u>) — you can be one of: <u>A</u>, <u>B</u>, <u>O</u> or <u>AB</u>.

2) These letters refer to the type of <u>antigens</u> on the surface of a person's <u>red blood cells</u>. (An antigen is a substance that can trigger a response from a person's <u>immune system</u>.)

3) Red blood cells can have <u>A or B antigens</u> (or <u>neither</u>, or <u>both</u>) on their surface.

4) And blood plasma can contain <u>anti-A or anti-B antibodies</u> (antibodies are chemicals produced by the immune system).

5) If <u>anti-A</u> antibodies <u>meet A</u> antigens OR <u>anti-B</u> antibodies <u>meet B</u> antigens the <u>blood will clot</u>.

Blood Group	Antigens	Antibodies
A	A	anti-B
B	B	anti-A
AB	A, B	none
O	none	anti-A, anti-B

You Can Test for Blood Group

When a <u>red stain</u> or substance is found at a crime scene scientists need to <u>test</u> whether it's <u>blood</u> (not, e.g. dye or ketchup). They then need to <u>test</u> if it's <u>human blood</u> (not from a dog or cat etc.) <u>Chemicals</u> are used to test for blood, then <u>anti-human antibodies</u> show if the blood is <u>human</u>. Once they've figured out it's human blood they can then test for the <u>blood group</u>:

1) Scientists can test for blood group by <u>mixing different antibodies</u> with <u>blood samples</u>.

2) Depending on whether the blood <u>clots</u> or <u>not</u> they can tell which blood type it is.

Blood Group	Antigens	Does it clot with anti-A antibodies?	Does it clot with anti-B antibodies?
A	A	Yes	No
B	B	No	Yes
AB	AB	Yes	Yes
O	none	No	No

E.g. if scientists add some <u>anti-A antibodies</u> to a blood sample and <u>it clots</u> then the blood group must be <u>either A</u> or <u>AB</u> (because it would only clot if A antigens were <u>present</u>). If they then added <u>anti-B antibodies</u> to the same blood and it didn't clot they would know it was blood <u>group A</u> (because if it had been AB then it would clot with anti-B antibodies).

If the blood group of the blood sample from the crime scene and the suspect's blood group <u>match</u> then your suspect <u>is still a suspect</u>. You <u>can't</u> say it's <u>definitely their blood</u> because there are only four blood types — so there are 1000s of other people that have the same blood type.

Blood typing — gets your keyboard a bit messy...

Blood typing isn't only important for forensics. It's really important in medicine too. For example, if you ever have a blood transfusion, the doctors have to make sure that the blood they give you is the right blood type.

DNA Profiling

Our <u>DNA</u> is what makes us <u>unique</u>. Analytical scientists can use DNA to help them <u>solve problems</u>.

DNA **is Unique**

DNA is a bit like a blueprint for how to make a human being.

1) <u>DNA</u> is the <u>genetic material</u> found in the <u>nucleus</u> of your <u>cells</u>.

2) Your DNA is <u>unique</u> — no one else in the world has the same DNA as you (unless you're an <u>identical twin</u>, then the two of you have <u>identical DNA</u>).

3) DNA can be <u>extracted</u> from <u>hair</u>, <u>skin flakes</u>, <u>blood</u>, <u>semen</u> and <u>saliva</u> because they all <u>contain cells</u>.

4) <u>DNA profiling</u> (or genetic fingerprinting) is a way of <u>comparing DNA samples</u> to see if they come from the same person or from two different people.

DNA Profiling **Pinpoints** Individuals

1) A sample of DNA is <u>split up</u> into <u>fragments</u> and then <u>separated out</u> in a process called <u>gel electrophoresis</u> (it's a bit like chromatography — see page 70) to produce a <u>DNA profile</u>.

2) You only need <u>very small amounts</u> of a sample to create a DNA profile using electrophoresis.

3) The <u>DNA profile</u> that is produced is usually <u>compared</u> with other DNA samples to find a <u>match</u>.

EXAMPLE

1) A drop of <u>blood</u> was found at a <u>crime scene</u>.
2) Forensic scientists ran a <u>DNA profile</u> for the blood.
3) They also ran DNA profiles for <u>two suspects</u>.
4) <u>Matching</u> DNA samples have the <u>same pattern</u> of bands. So here you can see that the blood from the crime scene has come from <u>suspect 2</u>.

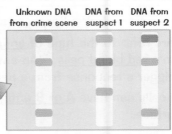

4) DNA profiling can also be used in <u>paternity tests</u> — to check if a man is the father of a particular child. This is because children <u>inherit</u> some of their DNA from their <u>mum</u> and some from their <u>dad</u> — so their DNA profiles will be <u>similar</u> to those of their parents.

5) <u>DNA profiling</u> is much more useful than <u>blood typing</u> in forensics. DNA profiling can tell you if the blood came from a <u>particular person</u>, whereas blood typing can only <u>narrow down</u> the possible suspects.

Higher — **HOW IT WORKS**

1) First you have to <u>extract</u> the DNA from the <u>cells</u> in the blood, semen etc.

2) The <u>DNA</u> is then <u>cut up</u> into <u>fragments</u>.

3) This produces lots of <u>different sized bits</u> of DNA. The number of each size will be <u>different for everyone</u> because of the way it's cut.

4) The DNA bits are <u>separated</u> by <u>size</u>, using <u>gel electrophoresis</u>. They're <u>suspended in an alkaline gel</u>, and an <u>electric current</u> is passed through the gel. DNA is <u>negatively charged</u> when it's in an <u>alkaline solution</u>, so it moves towards the <u>positively charged end</u> of the gel (because charged particles move in an electric field). Small bits travel <u>faster</u> than big bits, so they get <u>further</u> through the gel.

5) The DNA is then <u>treated</u> to make it <u>visible</u>.

DNA moves towards the positive end, with smallest fragments moving furthest

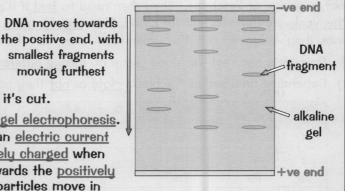

So the trick is — *frame your twin and they'll never get you...*

Some people think that <u>everyone's DNA profile</u> should be <u>stored</u> on a <u>database</u>. That way if a crime is committe all the police would have to do is search the database for a match to DNA found at the crime scene and, hey presto, they've got a suspect. However, many people are <u>against storing DNA profiles</u> because they think it's an <u>invasion of their privacy</u>, and that the government might use the information for <u>other purposes</u>.

Identifying Glass: Blocks

Identifying broken bits of glass and plastic can be really handy for tracking down suspects...

Glass and Plastic Can Refract Light

1) When light goes from one substance (or medium) into another substance, e.g. from air into glass, it gets refracted.

2) Refraction is when waves change direction as they enter a different medium.

3) This is caused entirely by the change in speed of the light waves.

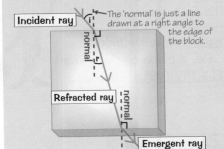

You can't fail to remember the old 'ray of light through a rectangular glass block' trick:

Incident ray

The 'normal' is just a line drawn at a right angle to the edge of the block.

Refracted ray

Emergent ray

1) The 'incident' ray is just the ray hitting the block.

2) It bends towards the normal as it enters the denser medium (the glass), and away from the normal as it emerges into the less dense medium (the air).

3) The angle between the normal and the incident ray is called the angle of incidence, i.

4) The angle between the normal and the refracted ray is called the angle of refraction, r.

Glass Can be Identified Using Its 'Refractive Index'

1) There are lots of different types of glass and clear plastic, and they all bend light by different amounts.

2) How much a material bends light is called its 'refractive index'.

3) The higher the refractive index, the more the light is bent as it passes from air into the material.

4) You can work out the refractive index, n, of a material using the formula below:

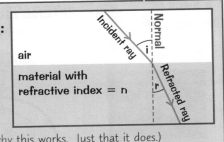

When a light ray passes into a material:

$$n = \frac{\sin i}{\sin r}$$

So if you know i and r, you can work out the refractive index.

air

material with refractive index = n

Incident ray   Normal

Refracted ray

(Thankfully you don't have to know why this works. Just that it does.)

TO FIND THE ANGLES OF INCIDENCE AND REFRACTION:

1) Draw a straight line on a piece of paper — this will be your 'normal'.

2) Place the block of glass or plastic carefully at right angles to the normal.

3) Shine a fine beam of light at the block so that it meets the block at an angle to the normal.

4) Using a protractor, carefully measure the angles of incidence and refraction.

5) So that's what 'refractive index' is, and you can use this method to work out the refractive index of a glass or plastic block. It's not a lot of good for criminal evidence though (unless someone's been nicking glass blocks from the glass block factory) — you tend to get small shards of glass instead.

You need to use a different method, which is covered on the next page.

Revise this — and make light work of it in the exam...

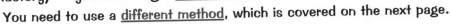

The basic ingredients of all glass are sodium carbonate, sand and limestone, but most common types of glass have added ingredients that affect the refractive index. For example, lead is added to some glass to make 'lead crystal'. This increases the refractive index of the glass and makes it 'sparklier'. Ooooooh.

Identifying Glass: Fragments

Once you know the refractive index of the glass from a <u>crime scene</u>, you can <u>compare</u> it with shards of glass found on the <u>clothes</u> or <u>shoes</u> of a suspect or on a suspect's <u>vehicle</u>. If they <u>match</u>, it suggests that they were at the crime scene. Most of the bits of glass you find on a suspect are <u>less than a millimetre</u> across though, which is a <u>bit small</u> for the method on the previous page — you'd have to have a <u>mighty small protractor</u>...

Finding the Refractive Index of Glass Fragments is Tricky...

1) You can only use the method shown on the previous page to find the refractive index of glass if the piece of glass is <u>big enough</u> — you need to be able to see the refracted beam clearly so you can measure the angle of refraction.

2) For <u>small pieces</u> or <u>shards</u> of glass you need to use this clever little fact:

> If you have <u>two materials</u> next to each other with the <u>same</u> refractive index, you <u>can't see the boundary (interface)</u> between them. So, a piece of glass in a liquid of the same refractive index would be <u>COMPLETELY INVISIBLE</u>. (Oooooh...)

You Use the Oil Immersion Temperature Method Instead

Some <u>oils</u>, e.g. <u>silicone oil</u>, have a refractive index that <u>changes</u> with <u>temperature</u>. You can vary the temperature of the oil until it has the same refractive index as your glass sample. Here's how it works:

1) Using <u>tweezers</u>, carefully place your tiny glass sample onto a <u>microscope slide</u>.

2) <u>Cover</u> the sample with a <u>few drops</u> of silicone oil (a clear, colourless liquid) and close the slide with a cover slip.

3) Push your slide into a piece of apparatus called a <u>hotstage</u>.

<u>HOTSTAGE:</u> used to warm the oil on the slide slowly and evenly.

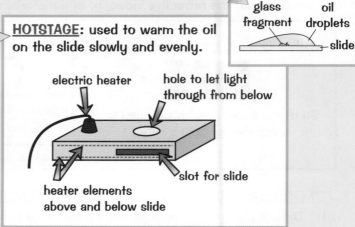

glass fragment — oil droplets — slide

electric heater

hole to let light through from below

slot for slide

heater elements above and below slide

4) Then put the whole thing under a <u>light microscope</u> (making sure the glass and the oil around it are well lit) and focus on the <u>boundary</u> between the glass and the oil.

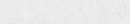
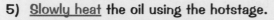

5) <u>Slowly heat</u> the oil using the hotstage.

6) As the <u>temperature</u> of the oil increases, it's refractive index <u>drops</u>. At a certain temperature, the boundary will <u>disappear</u> — the oil has the same refractive index as the glass.

You can then <u>look up</u> the refractive index of silicone oil at that temperature to find the refractive index of your glass sample.

In <u>modern</u> forensic labs, the observing is done by a <u>camera</u> attached to a <u>computer</u>. This is more <u>accurate</u> than observing the boundary by eye, since it doesn't rely on <u>human judgement</u>.

Hotstage — that's got to sting on panto night...

Of course, even if your bit of glass from the crime scene <u>matches</u> glass on the suspect, that <u>doesn't</u> mean they committed the crime. If the glass is <u>common</u>, the suspect could have picked it up somewhere else entirely. Or they could have been at the crime scene <u>without</u> committing the crime. Tricky...

Revision Summary for Section 7

Well, I bet after all that you fancy yourself a bit of a Miss Marple (how can I blame you — she has such marvellous fashion sense). But, to be a forensic scientist you need to know your stuff and not just accuse someone because they have a sinister beard, shifty walk or a white cat...

1) Define relative atomic mass and relative formula mass.

2)* Find the M_r of these (masses: H = 1, C = 12, N = 14, O = 16, K = 39):
   a) CO_2 b) KOH   c) NH_3

3)* What mass of calcium hydroxide ($Ca(OH)_2$) is produced when 50 g of calcium oxide (CaO) is reacted with water (H_2O)? Give your answer to 2 significant figures.
   Balanced equation: $CaO + H_2O \rightarrow Ca(OH)_2$, masses: Ca = 40, O = 16, H = 1.

4) Briefly describe how you would carry out an acid-base titration.

5) a)* Troy has 55 cm³ of a solution that contains an unknown concentration of hydrochloric acid (HCl). He does a titration and finds that it takes 30 cm³ of sodium hydroxide (NaOH) to neutralise the acid in the solution. The concentration of the sodium hydroxide is 0.1 moles per dm³. Find the concentration of hydrochloric acid in the solution. Balanced equation: $NaOH + HCl \rightarrow NaCl + H_2O$.
   b) Troy repeats the experiment three times and takes an average of his results. Why does he do this?

6) The diagram on the right shows a chromatogram produced from an unknown ink. Which dye, A, B or C, is the most soluble? Explain your answer.

7) A sample of ink from a forged document is compared to the samples of ink from the pens of 3 suspects. The results are shown in the diagram below. Which suspect do you think is most likely to have forged the document?

8)* What is the R_f value of a substance that moves 4.5 cm when the solvent moves 12 cm?

9) What is a comparison microscope? How is it used in forensic science?

10) Give three distinctive features of a seed.

11) Give three features that analytical scientists look at when comparing soil using a polarising microscope.

12) What do analytical scientists look for when comparing pollen samples?

13) Give three advantages of instrumental methods over traditional lab methods.

ink sample from forged document   ink from suspect A   ink from suspect B   ink from suspect C

14) What does the peak on a gas-liquid chromatogram represent?

15) Which diagram, A or B, shows the results of an infrared spectrometry analysis?

16) What are the four main components of blood?

17) What are the four blood groups?

18) A scientist tests a blood sample for blood group. They add anti-A antibodies and the blood does not clot. They then add anti-B antibodies and the blood does clot. What blood type is the sample?

A   **B**

19) Where in a cell is DNA found?

20) Describe the method used to make a DNA profile.

21) Draw a diagram to show the path of a ray of light as it passes from air → block of glass → air, meeting the block of glass at an angle to the normal. Mark on your diagram the angles of incidence and refraction.

22) Describe how you would find the refractive index of a glass block.

23) Explain why you can't usually use the method you described in the answer to Question 22 to find the refractive index of glass from a crime scene or suspect.

24) What method can forensic scientists use to find the refractive index of small pieces of glass? Explain how this method works.

* Answers on page 92.

Controlled Assessment Assignments

For Unit 2, you will have to complete two assignments — Assignment 1 and Assignment 2. Together they're worth 60% of your overall grade, eeeeek. Luckily there are a few pages coming up to help you out...

You Will Have to Complete *Two Assignments*

Those pesky examiners have come up with a (surprisingly) clever way of finding out whether you're any good at practical investigations and whether you understand what science is like in the real world...

Assignment 1

Assignment 1 is made up of two parts:

> 1) A research report on the work carried out by a scientist.
> 2) A practical investigation based on a technique that the scientist in your report might use.

There's loads more on Assignment 1 coming up on page 83.

Assignment 2 is worth a few more marks than Assignment 1.

Assignment 2

For Assignment 2 you will have to plan, carry out and write a report on a practical investigation that a scientist might do in the real world. Crikey. But don't worry, there's tonnes more stuff on page 84 to help you get your head around it.

Make Sure It's *All Your Own Work*

1) When you're writing your reports, make sure there's nobody else's work in with yours.
2) I know you're honest, but AQA take a very dim view of two candidates' work being too similar.
3) It's fine to include bits in your reports that come from books or websites, but you need to reference them — say where they come from.
4) You also need to work as independently as possible — your teacher can give you guidance, but they can't tell you what to write.

You've Got to Use *Good English — Alrite?*

Unfortunately for you, the examiners are well into their Quality of Written Communication (QWC) stuff. This just means that the examiner will assess your ability to write properly in the exam and in your report. This may seem like a bit of a drag but you might lose marks if you don't do it.

You need to make sure that:

1) Your scribble, sorry, writing is legible (make sure it's easy to read).
2) Your spelling, punctuation and grammar are accurate.
3) Your writing style is appropriate.
4) You write clearly and coherently (so it's easy to understand).
5) You use the proper scientific terms (words) where it's appropriate.

Don't forget that you'll be tested on QWC in your exam as well as in your assignments.

Reports, investigations? Who do you think you are? — Poirot?

This report writing malarkey isn't as bad as it first appears. Honest. All you have to do is use your common sense and make sure that your reports contain all of the lovely stuff found on pages 83 and 84...

Researching the Role of a Scientist

This page is crammed full of useful tips to help you get the best mark possible for Assignment 1.
Assignment 1 is all about investigating the work of scientists and how they use science.

There are Loads of Different Jobs a Scientist Can Do

There are loads of scientists in our society and they can do very different jobs...

1) Classification — for example, some scientists spend their time studying new plants or new diseases.

2) Mining — scientists are needed to help drill for oil or mine for precious metals.

3) Production — scientists are always involved in designing and making new materials.
E.g. developing high strength glass to withstand machine gun fire.

4) Problem Solving — governments and businesses employ scientists to solve problems that they can't solve themselves. This could be things like working out how to reduce pollution or how to send people to Mars.

5) Monitoring and Controlling — scientists are often employed to monitor and control processes.
For example, making sure chocolate bars always taste the same and are the same size.

There are Four Types of Scientist You Could Write About

For Assignment 1 you will have to research a type of scientist and prepare a report on their work.
There are four types of scientist that you might have to look at:

HEALTHCARE SCIENTISTS

For example, doctor   dietician

pharmacist   physiotherapist   nurse

ANALYTICAL SCIENTISTS

For example,   environmental scientist

forensic scientist   pharmaceutical researcher

MATERIALS SCIENTISTS

For example,   biomaterials specialist

polymer chemist   ceramics scientist

FOOD SCIENTISTS

For example,   microbiologist   nutritionist

agricultural scientist   dietician

You Have to do an Experiment Based on the Scientist's Work...

1) As well as researching the role of one of the scientists shown above, you'll be given an investigation and will have to come up with a hypothesis for it (see page 1).

2) You'll have to carry out the investigation (using standard procedures, see page 2) to test your hypothesis.

3) Finally you'll have to analyse the results of your experiment and come up with a conclusion (see page 89).

...Then You're Gonna Have to Write it all Up

When you're writing your report for Assignment 1, make sure you include:

1) Loads of stuff on the work of the scientist.

2) The role of the organisation your scientist works for and how the research benefits society.

3) The qualifications the scientist needs to do their job.

4) How the scientist uses their knowledge and practical skills in their work.

5) A bibliography showing where all your information comes from — this bit's really important so don't forget it.

You'll also need to include a write up of your experiment — there's more on how to do this on pages 87-89.

Assignment 1 — a report of two halves...

So I guess what we've learnt from this page is that scientists are waaaaay cooler than everyone seems to think.
It's amazing how many of the jobs out there are done by scientists — even this book was written by scientists.

How Scientists Use Evidence to Solve Problems

For Assignment 2 you're gonna have to carry out an <u>investigation</u> to solve a <u>problem</u> and then write a <u>report</u> all about it. Sounds fun, eh? Make sure you cover all the points on this page when you're writing your report and you'll be teacher's pet before you know it. Oh the joys.

Include All These Points When You Write Your Report

Here are the things that your report should contain:

1) A description of why you're doing your investigation

Think about <u>why</u> a scientist would need to carry out an experiment like this. What will it help them to discover? Will it help to solve a problem? Include your <u>hypothesis</u> in this section (see page 1).

2) A plan of how you're going to carry out your investigation

Think about what <u>equipment</u> you will need and how you will make your investigation <u>fair</u>. Check out page 85 for more on planning.

3) A risk assessment

You need to make sure you that you've spotted all the <u>risks</u> and worked out how you're going to <u>minimise the danger</u>. There's loads more on this on page 4 and page 85.

4) A record of the data you collect

Make sure that you include all the results of you experiment and of any <u>trial runs</u> too. Check that your data's <u>accurate</u>, <u>reliable</u> and <u>reproducible</u>. More on this on page 86.

5) A section on how you processed your data

Remember to include whether you have any <u>anomalous results</u> in this bit. You also need to <u>present</u> your final data nicely. See pages 87-88 for more.

6) An analysis of your data

Explain what you think your data <u>shows</u>. You need to draw <u>conclusions based on the data</u> you've collected. Page 89 has more on this.

Drake's conclusion:
electricity = bad hair.

7) An evaluation of your investigation

Try to think about what went <u>well</u>, what went <u>badly</u> and what you would <u>change</u> if you were going to do the investigation again. This is covered on page 89.

8) An explanation of how a scientist might use the results of the investigation

For example, will the results help to crack a <u>murder investigation</u>? Will they help to find out <u>what a substance is</u>? Will they help to <u>diagnose an illness</u>? Will they help to work out if a food is <u>safe to eat</u>?

Writing reports? — I thought this was Science not English...

There's no magic number of words that your report must be — it has to be long enough to get your <u>point across clearly</u>, but not so long that you fill it with <u>waffle</u>. Good luck.

Planning an Investigation

Here's how practical investigations should be carried out — by both professional scientists and you.
You'll need to know this stuff for Assignment 1 and Assignment 2.

To Make an Investigation a Fair Test You Have to Control the Variables

An investigation is a way of finding out whether or not two variables (things) are related.
Investigations that you plan should always be a fair test.

1) In a lab experiment you usually change one thing (a variable) and measure how it affects another thing (another variable).

> **EXAMPLE:** you might change only the temperature and measure how it affects the rate of bacterial growth.

2) Everything else that could affect the results needs to stay the same.
Then you know that the thing you're changing is the only thing that's affecting the results.

> **EXAMPLE continued:** everything apart from the temperature needs to be kept the same — the substance the bacteria is grown on, the type of bacteria, the amount of moisture etc. If it isn't, you won't know if any change in the rate of growth is caused by the change in temperature, or something else.

3) The variable that you change is called the independent variable.

4) The variable that's measured is called the dependent variable.

5) The variables you keep the same are called control variables.

> **EXAMPLE continued:**
> Independent = temperature
> Dependent = rate of bacteria growth
> Controls = substance bacteria grown on, type of bacteria, moisture level, etc.

The Equipment Used has to be Right for the Job

1) You need to make sure you choose the right equipment.

2) For example, the measuring equipment you use has to be sensitive enough to accurately measure the chemicals you're using. If you need to measure out 11 ml of a liquid, use a measuring cylinder that can measure to 1 ml, not 5 or 10 ml.

3) You should also be able to explain why you've chosen each bit of kit.

> Accurate measurements are really close to the true value of what you're measuring.

Experiments Must be Safe

1) There are lots of hazards (dangers) you could be faced with during an investigation, e.g. radiation, electricity, gas, chemicals and fire.

2) You should always make sure that you think of all the hazards there might be.

3) You should also come up with ways of reducing the risks from the hazards you've spotted.

4) For example, for an experiment involving a Bunsen burner:

5) There's more about writing risk assessments on page 4.

> Hazard:
> • Bunsen burner is a fire risk.
> Ways risk can be reduced:
> • Keep chemicals that can catch fire away from the Bunsen.
> • Never leave the Bunsen alone when lit.
> • Always turn on the yellow safety flame when not in use.

Hazard: revision boredom. Reduce by: using CGP books

Now, all this even before you've started the investigation — it really does make them run more smoothly though.

Getting the Data Right

You'll want to make sure that you get the best results you possibly can. Here are a few things you can do:

Data Should be as Reliable, Accurate and Precise as Possible

1) Reliable results are results that always come out the same every time you do the same experiment.

2) If your results are reliable they're more likely to be true. This means you can have more trust in your conclusions.

3) You can make your results more reliable by repeating the readings at least twice (so that you have at least three readings). Then you can calculate the mean (that's the average — see next page).

4) Checking your results match with secondary sources, e.g. studies that other people have done, also makes your data more reliable.

5) You should also always make sure that your results are accurate.

6) Really accurate results are those that are really close to the true answer.

7) You can get accurate results by making sure the equipment you're using is sensitive enough (see previous page).

8) Your data also needs to be precise. How precise your data is depends on the scale that your instrument measures to. For example, a ruler that measures in mm will give you more precise data than one that measures in cm and a reading of, for example, 37.45 °C is more precise than a reading of 37 °C.

You Can Check For Mistakes Made When Collecting Data

1) When you've collected all the results for an experiment, you should have a look to see if there are any results that don't seem to fit in with the rest.

2) Most results are slightly different, but any that are totally different are called anomalous results.

3) They're mainly caused by human errors, e.g. by a whoopsie when measuring.

4) The only way to stop them happening is by taking all your measurements as carefully as possible.

5) If you ever get any anomalous results, you should try to work out what happened.

6) If you can work out what happened (e.g. you measured something wrong) you can repeat the measurement making sure that you don't make the same mistake again.

7) Slightly odd data could also be caused by instrument errors, e.g. using a ruler which has wonky markings.

Round Your Data to the Correct Number of Significant Figures

It's important to give any data you collect to the correct number of significant figures (s.f.).

1) The first significant figure of a number is the first digit that isn't a zero.

2) The second, third and fourth significant figures follow on immediately after the first (even if they are zeros).

3) You should always record data to an appropriate number of s.f. — if your instruments only measure to 1 s.f. only give the data in your report to 1 s.f.

4) If you're doing a calculation you should give your data to the lowest number of s.f. used in the calculation.

> **Example**
>
> A metal bar has a cross sectional area of 0.52 m². A force of 2 N is applied to the bar. Calculate the stress felt by the bar.
>
> The lowest number of s.f. in the question is 1 s.f. so you need to give your answer to 1 s.f. too.
>
> Stress = Force ÷ Area = 2 ÷ 0.52 = 4 Nm⁻² (1 s.f.)

Reliable data — it won't ever forget your birthday...

All this stuff is really important — your data will be meaningless if it's not reliable and accurate. So give this page a read through a couple of times and your data will be the envy of all the scientists in the world. Yes, all of them.

Processing and Presenting Data

The fun doesn't stop once you've collected your data — it then needs to be **processed** and **presented**...

Data **Needs to be** Organised

1) Data that's been collected needs to be <u>organised</u> so it can be processed later on.

2) <u>Tables</u> are dead useful for <u>organising data</u>.

3) You should always make sure that <u>each column</u> has a <u>heading</u> and that you've included the <u>units</u>.

Test tube	Result (ml)	Repeat 1 (ml)	Repeat 2 (ml)
A	28	37	32
B	47	51	60
C	68	72	70

Data **Can be** Processed **Using a Bit of** Maths

1) <u>Raw data</u> just isn't that useful. To make it useful, you have to <u>process</u> it in some way.

2) One of the most simple calculations you can do is the <u>mean</u> (average):

> To calculate the <u>mean</u> <u>ADD TOGETHER</u> all the data values. Then <u>DIVIDE</u> by the total number of values. You usually do this to get a single value from several <u>repeats</u> of your experiment.

Test tube	Result (ml)	Repeat 1 (ml)	Repeat 2 (ml)	Mean (ml)
A	28	37	32	$(28 + 37 + 32) \div 3 = 32.3$
B	47	51	60	$(47 + 51 + 60) \div 3 = 52.7$
C	68	72	70	$(68 + 72 + 70) \div 3 = 70.0$

Different Types **of** Data **Should be** Presented **in** Different Ways

1) You need to <u>present</u> your data so that it's easier to see any <u>patterns</u>.

2) Different types of investigations give you <u>different types</u> of data, so you'll always have to <u>choose</u> what the best way to present your data is.

Pie charts can be used to present the same sort of data as bar charts. They're mostly used when the data is in percentages or fractions.

Bar Charts

1) If the independent variable comes in <u>clear categories</u> (e.g. blood types, metals) you should use a <u>bar chart</u> to display the data.

2) You also use them if the independent variable can be counted in <u>chunks</u>, where there are no in-between values. For example, number of people (because you can't have half a person).

3) There are some <u>golden rules</u> you need to follow for <u>drawing</u> bar charts:

Remember to include the <u>units</u>.

Label both axes.

Ice Cream Sales in Fishland and Cheeseland

Number sold (thousands) — Ice cream flavour: Chocolate, Mint, Strawberry, Broccoli

Key: Fishland, Cheeseland

If there's more than one set of data <u>include a key</u>.

Draw it nice and <u>big</u>.

Leave a <u>gap between</u> different categories.

Presenting Data

Line Graphs

If the independent variable can have <u>any value</u> within a <u>range</u>, (e.g. length, volume, temperature) you should use a <u>line graph</u> to display the data.

Remember to include the <u>units</u>.

The <u>dependent</u> variable (the thing you measure) goes on the <u>y-axis</u> (the <u>vertical</u> one).

The <u>independent</u> variable (the thing you change) goes on the <u>x-axis</u> (the <u>horizontal</u> one).

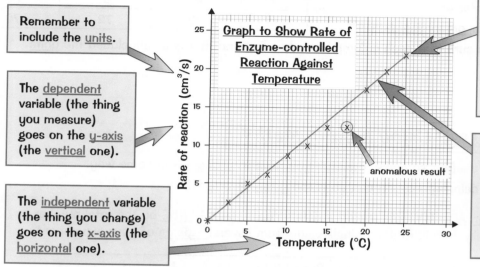

Graph to Show Rate of Enzyme-controlled Reaction Against Temperature

anomalous result

When plotting points, use a <u>sharp pencil</u> and make a <u>neat little cross</u> (don't do blobs).

nice clear mark   smudged unclear marks

<u>Don't join the dots up</u>. You should draw a <u>line of best fit</u> (or a <u>curve of best fit</u>). Try to draw the line <u>through</u> or as <u>near</u> to <u>as many points as possible</u>, ignoring anomalous results.

Line Graphs Can Show Patterns in Data

1) <u>Line graphs</u> are great for showing <u>patterns</u> in data.

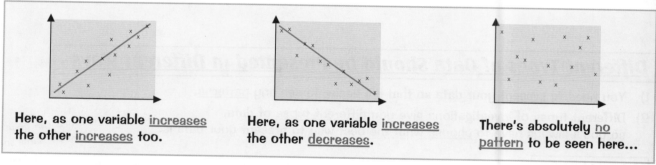

Here, as one variable <u>increases</u> the other <u>increases</u> too.

Here, as one variable <u>increases</u> the other <u>decreases</u>.

There's absolutely <u>no</u> <u>pattern</u> to be seen here...

2) You might see these three patterns — they've got special names...

<u>LINEAR</u> — the graph is a <u>straight line</u>.

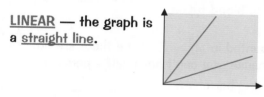

<u>DIRECTLY PROPORTIONAL</u> — the graph is a <u>straight line</u> where both variables increase (or decrease) in the <u>same ratio</u>.

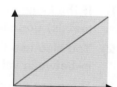

<u>COMPLEX RELATIONSHIP</u> — the graph clearly shows a pattern but it's not a straight line.

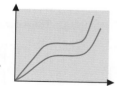

3) If there's a <u>pattern</u> between two variables, it doesn't mean that one is <u>causing</u> the other to change. It just means they're <u>related</u> in some way. There could be <u>something else</u> causing the change.

As age of man increases, length of nose hair also increases...

<u>Process</u>, <u>present</u>, <u>interpret</u>... data's like a difficult child — it needs a lot of attention. Go on, make it happy.

How Scientists Use Practical Techniques

Concluding and Evaluating

At the end of an investigation, the <u>conclusion</u> and <u>evaluation</u> are waiting. Don't worry, they won't bite.

A Conclusion is a Summary of What You've Learnt

1) Once you've collected, presented and analysed your data, you need to come to a <u>conclusion</u>.

2) You just have to <u>look at your data</u> and <u>say what pattern you see</u>.

> **EXAMPLE:** The table on the right shows the heights of pea plant seedlings grown for three weeks with different fertilisers.
>
> | Fertiliser | Mean growth (mm) |
> |---|---|
> | A | 13.5 |
> | B | 19.5 |
> | No fertiliser | 5.5 |
>
> <u>CONCLUSION</u>: Fertiliser <u>B</u> makes <u>pea plant</u> seedlings grow taller over a <u>three week</u> period than fertiliser A.

3) You also need to use the data that's been <u>collected</u> to <u>justify</u> the conclusion (back it up).

> **EXAMPLE** continued: Fertiliser B made the pea plants grow 6 mm more on average than fertiliser A.

4) It's important that the conclusion <u>doesn't say anything that the data doesn't show</u>.

> **EXAMPLE** continued: You can't conclude that fertiliser B makes <u>any other type of plant</u> grow taller than fertiliser A — the results could be totally different.

5) You should also use your own <u>scientific knowledge</u> (the stuff you've learnt) to try to <u>explain</u> the conclusion.

Evaluation — Describe How it Could be Improved

I'd value this E somewhere in the region of 250-300k

In an evaluation you look back over the whole investigation.

1) You should comment on the <u>method</u> — was the <u>equipment suitable</u>? Was it a <u>fair test</u>?

2) Comment on the <u>quality</u> of the <u>results</u> — were they <u>reliable</u> and <u>accurate</u>?

3) Say whether your data is <u>valid</u> — is it <u>reliable</u> and is it <u>evidence</u> for or against the <u>original hypothesis</u>?

4) If there were any anomalous results, try to <u>explain</u> them — were they caused by <u>errors</u> in measurement?

5) When you look back at your investigation like this, you'll be able to say how <u>sure</u> you are that your conclusion is <u>right</u>.

6) Then you can suggest any <u>changes</u> that would <u>improve</u> the quality of the results. For example, you might suggest changing the way you controlled a variable, or changing the interval of values you measured.

7) This would mean you could be <u>more sure</u> about your conclusion.

8) When you suggest an improvement, always say <u>why</u> you think this would make the results <u>better</u>.

The Last Part of Your Report Should Relate to the Real World

1) At the end of <u>Assignment 2</u> you need to research <u>how</u> your investigation could be used in the <u>real world</u>.

2) You need to <u>explain how</u> a scientist might use the <u>results</u> of the experiment.

> Fertiliser example continued: The scientist conducting the investigation could tell farmers using fertiliser A on their pea plants that switching to fertiliser B could make them grow more quickly.

aluation — in my next study I will make sure I don't burn the lab down...

ow it doesn't seem very nice, but writing about where you went <u>wrong</u> is an important skill. It shows you've a really good understanding of what the investigation was <u>about</u>. It's difficult for me — I'm always right.

Index

Index

Index and Answers

Answers

Revision Summary for Section 2 (page 23)

33) $75 \times 24 \times 5.4 = 9720$ kJ/day

35) $85 \div 1.8^2 = 26.2$

Revision Summary for Section 3 (page 35)

4) C

8) Density = mass ÷ volume = $30 \div 20 = 1.5$ g/cm^3

Revision Summary for Section 4 (page 44)

18) If six colonies grew from one tenth of the final dilution, there were approximately:
60 bacteria in the final dilution,
600 bacteria in the second dilution,
6000 bacteria in the first dilution.

So 1 cm^3 of the milkshake contained approximately <u>6000 bacteria</u>.

Revision Summary for Section 5 (page 54)

19) percentage yield =
(actual yield ÷ theoretical yield) × 100
= $(2400 \div 3000) \times 100$
= $0.8 \times 100 = 80\%$

Bottom of page 57

a) MgO

b) Li_2O

c) Na_2SO_4

Revision Summary for Section 6 (page 65)

6) a) FeO

b) Fe_2O_3

c) $CaCl_2$

d) Na_2CO_3

19) a) barium sulfate + iron(II) chloride

b) silver chloride + zinc nitrate

22) a) The blue precipitate means it contains copper. The white precipitate means it contains sulfate ions. The powder is copper sulfate.

b) $CuSO_4$

23) a) $CaCO_3 + 2HCl \rightarrow CaCl_2 + H_2O + CO_2$

b) $Ca + 2H_2O \rightarrow Ca(OH)_2 + H_2$

Bottom of page 66

NaOH: 40, Fe_2O_3: 160, C_6H_{14}: 86

Bottom of page 67

40 g of Ca reacts to give 56 g of CaO.
0.7 g of Ca reacts to give 1 g of CaO.
So, <u>21 g</u> of Ca reacts to give 30 g of CaO.

Revision Summary for Section 7 (page 81)

2) a) 44   b) 56   c) 17

3) 56 g of CaO reacts to give 74 g of $Ca(OH)_2$
1 g of CaO reacts to give 1.3 g of $Ca(OH)_2$
50 g of CaO reacts to give <u>66 g</u> of $Ca(OH)_2$

5) a) moles of NaOH = concentration × volume
= $0.1 \times (30 \div 1000)$
= 0.003 moles
1 mole of NaOH reacts with 1 mole of HCl so there must be 0.003 moles of HCl.
concentration of HCl = moles ÷ volume
= $0.003 \div (55 \div 1000)$
= 0.05 moles per dm^3

8) $R_f = 4.5 \div 12 = 0.38$